TENDER IS THE SCALPEL'S EDGE

Tender is the Scalpel's Edge

Glimpses from the Journal
of an NHS Consultant Surgeon

Gautam Das

Matador
9 Priory Business Park,
Wistow Road, Kibworth Beauchamp,
Leicestershire. LE8 0RX
Tel: 0116 279 2299
Email: books@troubador.co.uk
Web: www.troubador.co.uk/matador
Twitter: @matadorbooks

ISBN 978 1785898 440

British Library Cataloguing in Publication Data.
A catalogue record for this book is available from the British Library.

Printed and bound in the UK by TJ International, Padstow, Cornwall
Typeset in 11pt Minion Pro by Troubador Publishing Ltd, Leicester, UK

Matador is an imprint of Troubador Publishing Ltd

For Kamala: mother, high school teacher, Durga

and

Manindra: husband and father, who cherished us both

The unexamined life is not worth living

Socrates, circa 399 BC

A good surgeon is an operating physician

Satvinder Singh Mudan FRCS
Senior Consultant Surgeon
The Royal Marsden Hospital London,
who first made this incisive and insightful
observation in 1990 as a surgical registrar
at the Mayday Hospital, Croydon

Preface

From somewhere within came the intense urge to tell these stories about people, amazing in their own ways, hidden as they have been in deep vaults, some as far back as fifty years. It is more than just an account of harsh clinical facts, it is the thoughts, perceptions and emotions that I have tried to portray in these stories.

I have also endeavoured to show how powerfully fascinating it is to be a surgeon. That once the impulse has been sparked, there is no looking back.

The surgical life is all-consuming, you take your worries home and wake up with them, though like every other surgeon, I wouldn't wish for any other existence. If this book provides even a modicum of understanding of the thoughts, feelings, fears and joys that animate such a life, I will humbly accept it as a success. If reading the book encourages a young mind to start on the surgical path, the book will have achieved the highest measure of fulfilment.

The identity of all the patients have been carefully protected and confidentiality strictly ensured by changing names and dates, often locations, as well as altering age, gender and ethnicity.

Gautam Das, Surrey

CONTENTS

CHAPTER 1

Emma

Mayday Hospital, Croydon – 1996

I was the senior urology surgeon on-call when Emma was brought to Mayday Hospital as an emergency that Sunday morning in December.

Every other day of the week, and every other weekend, I was the duty consultant for Croydon patients admitted with serious urological conditions – the distressed elderly man in worsening pain and panic, unable to pee, his urethra choked by an enlarged prostate; the restless, feverish young woman, acutely ill from a severe kidney infection; the tearful little boy, woken from sleep by the dreadful pain of a torted testis.

Far less common would be the person brought to our A&E with an injury to the kidney following a road traffic accident or assault. Nonetheless, when such an eventuality did occur, prompt assessment was a must – given that although most patients with kidney trauma settle with bed rest, intravenous fluids and close monitoring, a small, though critically important percentage, need an urgent operation.

*

That weekend was my last on-call before Christmas. It had been relatively quiet with not many emergency admissions. On the Sunday morning, not even a telephone call disturbed the tranquility of Grove House, in the Surrey village of Woldingham.

There was no familiar 'Hello Mr Das, Trudy from switchboard here, surgical registrar needs a word.'

I wanted to go into Croydon town centre to make a start on an important task which I'd kept putting off – Christmas shopping.

Before that, I had to drop into Bensham 2, our urology ward, to check on patients that I'd recently operated on.

I clipped on my pager – three bars showed that the battery was full – before leaving Grove House for Mayday Hospital.

When I went into Bensham 2, all seemed quiet. Many of our patients were waiting to go home, having recovered from surgery carried out earlier in the week. There were no problems with the others, and my ward round didn't take long.

As I was about to leave, the telephone on the nursing desk rang and was answered by Audrey Lemay, staff nurse in charge. Instinct made me wait. Audrey listened attentively for a minute, then looked up at me as if to say, 'Don't go, this one's important.'

She put down the receiver and said, 'They've got a suspected renal trauma that was brought into casualty about an hour ago. Someone saw you in the staff car park and thought it best to let you know.'

'Is the patient still in A&E?' I asked.

'She's just been moved to intensive care. That was Sister Morell on the phone.'

I went into the corridor outside the ward and headed straight for the stairwell down to intensive care one floor below.

As I went down the flight of stairs, people coming up, gave me a wide berth. On the ground floor of the surgical wing, I pushed open the swing doors and entered the controlled calm of ITU. All eight beds were occupied. The one nearest to the nursing desk had its curtains drawn.

Roger, the charge nurse on duty, was changing an intravenous infusion drip at another bed. He had a white plastic apron, tied at the back, protecting the front of his dark blue uniform. The flimsy material of the disposable apron rustled as he reached up to replace the fluid bag hanging from the top of the drip stand.

Roger pointed to the nursing desk with his free hand. 'Be with you in just a sec, Mr Das.'

As I placed my briefcase on the desktop and lowered myself into an armless orange plastic chair, the drawn curtains of the bed nearby were sharply pulled open with a metallic screech – my gaze fell upon a young woman lying motionless on the bed.

The two most striking features of the tableau were the pure white of the woman's face and bare arms, contrasting sharply with the bright crimson that filled a visible length of transparent tubing connected to a catheter bag fixed on hooks at the bedside.

The stark contrast of the deathly pallor of her face and the thick red blood in the catheter tube jolted an instantaneous frisson in my mind.

I was conscious of the first shiver of apprehension, bordering on fear.

My focus took in the intravenous line connected to the cannula taped to the inside of her forearm – the crystal-clear drops of Hartmann's solution hurriedly falling in the transparent drip chamber with the urgency of a heavy rain shower, agitating the floating anti-embolism ball inside.

Sarah, our experienced year-five surgical registrar who'd been attending to the young woman, saw me at the desk. She nodded and came over.

'This girl Emma was brought into A&E with severe left-sided pain. Said that she and her boyfriend were horsing around, and she accidentally got kicked.'

Sarah glanced at her patient.

'She felt sudden pain, that quickly got worse, and then she started passing blood. Boyfriend called an ambulance. He's sitting outside, worried sick, and feeling sorry for himself.'

'Has she had any imaging?' I asked.

'We've done an IVU and ultrasound. I've requested an urgent CT.'

(In those days, apart from cases of head injury, you didn't have the godsend of CT scanning immediately available in casualty, as we do now.)

The ultrasound scan and the IVU (intravenous urogram) dye test showed a large collection of blood around an indistinctly outlined left kidney. The right looked perfectly normal, as did the spleen and liver.

Sarah and I walked over to the bedside and looked at the charts – Emma's vital signs of pulse and blood pressure were fine. She didn't have a low dipping BP and fast pulse rate, signs of shock from blood loss. For the time being at least, she appeared to be, in medical terminology, "haemodynamically stable".

I looked at Emma as I stood at the bedside. Her eyes were closed, she seemed to be asleep; tranquil, for the time being, from the analgesics she'd been given.

I said to Sarah, 'I just don't like the look of her. She's too pale, and obviously that's fresh blood in her catheter tube. What's her haemoglobin?'

'It's fine; it was twelve when we checked on admission.'

'That's nearly an hour ago. It doesn't fit with her pallor. I'd like an urgent Hb now,' I said.

'OK, will do.' Sarah pulled out a request form. 'Why don't you go home? I'll page you with the latest results.'

'No, I'm not going anywhere till I see that urgent Hb result. I'll pop upstairs to the office, and you can call me as soon as you have it.' I looked again at our patient. 'By the way, do we have an interventional radiologist for an embolisation?'

(Embolisation is a highly effective minimally invasive procedure, whereby the interventional radiologist snakes a fine tube inside a bleeding artery, and blocks it off by injecting tiny platinum coils that plug the artery, thereby staunching the haemorrhage. Nowadays, interventional radiology has made great progress and is much more readily available even outside of large teaching hospitals.)

'We haven't got one on-site today.'

I picked up my briefcase. 'Also, better warn theatres and the anaesthetists that we have a potential emergency. We may have to take her to theatres at very short notice.'

*

I sat down at my crowded office desk, but couldn't settle. I gave a cursory glance at the stack of dictation letters, the mound of case notes, a bulging in-tray of GP referrals that stared accusingly, demanding to be sorted.

I kept looking at the office phone, sitting stubbornly mute on the desktop next to the computer, willing the damn thing to ring.

I forced myself to make a start on marking the referral letters.

I'd picked up the second, perhaps the third, when the phone rang, startling me. I snatched the handset – a bored voice said that she was one of the weekend temps at medical records, checking to see if she could come up for a set of notes needed for the Monday clinic. I just about succeeded in keeping the brusqueness out of my terse reply.

Shortly after the young temp had left with her precious set of notes, the phone rang again.

This time it was Sarah.

'Haemoglobin's down to nine. I've set up a transfusion of two units of blood and have cross-matched four more.'

'This can't wait,' I said sharply. 'She's dropped her Hb three points in less than an hour, she's pouring blood from that kidney – we've got to open her up. I'm on my way to theatres. Meet me there.'

There was no choice here. I had to operate immediately to stop the bleeding which had caused the precipitous fall in Emma's haemoglobin.

Our superb on-call theatre team swung into action. By the time I'd raced up to theatres on the top floor, the nursing staff were ready and waiting.

I poked my head through the swing doors of Theatre 2 and was relieved to see Charity, one of our regular senior theatre sisters already scrubbed, checking a trolley of surgical instruments. There's nothing more trying than having to work with unfamiliar "bank" staff, temporary workers who come and go, when you're facing a challenging case.

Charity had brought out the large general abdominal pack of instruments, as well as the vascular set in anticipation of a difficult operation. She knew from long experience that once the abdomen was opened, events would move at a furious pace. Artery forceps, special vascular clamps, swabs of varying sizes, ties and sutures would all be demanded, and expected to be handed over instantaneously.

There wouldn't be a pre-determined or predictable sequence during this emergency operation. In the taut atmosphere, commands would be sharp. Without speaking a single word or looking up from the operative field, the surgeon or first assistant would stretch out his hand, expecting the correct instrument to be placed with an audible snap on a gloved open palm. There would be no room for dithering. The critical operation that we were about to start would test the surgical team to the extreme, with little margin for error.

(As noted earlier, injuries to the kidney are relatively rare in Britain. Most can be safely managed by "conservative" measures and close observation.)

With Emma, we did not have the comfort of a "wait and watch" policy. She had a severe injury, and was bleeding rapidly towards a fatal outcome.

(From experience, we also knew that severely damaged kidneys cannot be saved – they need to be removed swiftly, before the patient bleeds to death.)

The urgency that we faced demanded speedy action.

Nonetheless, unless one is in a battlefield situation, safe surgery necessitates an irreducible minimum of preparation including assessment by the anaesthetic team.

In that short time, we ordered more blood. A pre-emptive request for fresh frozen plasma was also telephoned through to our blood bank in Tooting.

I called Ian Swift, my general surgery consultant colleague, who was also on-call that weekend. It is always advantageous to have a senior colleague nearby, for a difficult operation. It's more than helpful to know that someone experienced is there, to jump in and assist if things really get out of hand. For a surgeon, there exists one sound that is more frightening than cannon-fire – the angry bruit of an uncontrolled major arterial bleed, where the more senior the help available, the better it is.

Ian had just left the hospital, having himself finished an emergency operation on an eighty-year-old woman with an obstructed large intestine. He answered his mobile phone at the second ring.

'Sorry to bother, Ian. Got a renal trauma that I'm taking to theatre, could do with a bit of backup.'

'No worries, be there straight away.'

*

Sarah and I started the operation. I picked up a scalpel and made a long midline incision on the abdomen, starting from a point just below the xiphisternum down to the belly-button. A thin wake of blood followed the skin incision. It didn't have the viscous consistency of normal blood – this was an attenuated trickle.

'Hell, this blood's like water. What's the haemoglobin now?'

I looked up at Katty Ansari, our anaesthetic consultant.

In a quiet voice, Katty said, 'Hb's down to 5.6.'

This confirmed that there was an open tap inside Emma's abdomen leaking blood, inexorably pulling her life down a sink-hole.

We opened the abdomen with our sweeping midline incision, rapidly entering the peritoneal cavity. Fortunately, there was no free blood inside, suggesting that the other internal organs were unharmed. We quickly checked the spleen and liver to confirm that they were intact.

Carefully moving aside loops of intestine, and covering them with large wet swabs, we could clearly see a huge blue-black mass pushing up from the back of the open abdomen, the area called the retroperitoneum.

We quickly mobilised the descending colon, which lies in front of the left kidney, and pushed it away to gain access to the front of the kidney with its finger-thick blood vessels, the renal artery and renal vein, taking great care not to inadvertently injure the spleen which lies close to the top left corner of the colon.

The huge mass made up of an enlarging collection of blood and clots from the injured kidney was now right in front of us. It was tightly contained by the thin membrane of the posterior parietal peritoneum which covers the front of the kidneys. The mass seemed to be expanding before our eyes, almost throbbing, as though in suppressed rage.

Deep inside was the ruptured kidney – the leaking faucet.

(Our kidneys take up a quarter of the entire cardiac output. With every heartbeat, the left ventricle contracts powerfully, pumping out oxygenated blood to the body. A full quarter of that ejected blood goes straight to the kidneys. A torn renal artery hoses like a pressure jet.)

We had to turn off the tap quickly to stop Emma from exsanguinating.

'I'm going to cut into this bloody thing now,' I said aloud. 'And it's going to bleed like stink.'

What was also worrying me was that the mass was expanding from the left side across the midline towards Emma's healthy right kidney. The danger was that the right renal vein would be caught up, and once the mass was opened, tissue planes around vital structures would be flooded with blood and clots. In that melee, the right renal vein would be difficult to identify and safeguard. It would be at risk of an accidental tear – leaving Emma with her remaining kidney damaged, requiring dialysis – that is, if she survived.

I looked across into Sarah's eyes and said, 'We'll have to be really careful not to prang the right renal vein. That'd be an absolute fucking disaster.'

*

The adrenaline-driven tension in an urgent situation such as this, paradoxically, calms the mind. The understanding and acceptance that there's no other option, that pusillanimity would lead to tragedy, helps steady frayed nerves. Moreover, being helped by a competent first assistant is indispensable in a hazardous situation – an assistant who is intuitive, who knows what to do without being prompted, a co-pilot who can read your mind and has the gift of anticipation.

I picked up curved Metzenbaum scissors to open the retroperitoneal haematoma.

'You ready?' I asked, looking at Sarah – she was, armed with large swabs and Yankauer sucker.

As I incised the taut peritoneal integument, a pyroclastic surge of clots and blood erupted and instantaneously filled the operative field. We scooped out clumps of blood clots by the handful. Sarah deftly mopped the spilled blood with large swabs, simultaneously deploying the sucker tube. The hiss and gurgle of the sucker machine was the only audible sound in theatres. We worked together in harmonious tandem, with controlled swiftness, and resisted the temptation to glance at the chilling number of blood-soaked swabs being hooked up on the swab count board, and the alarming rise of the red meniscus in the glass sucker bottle.

No one spoke in Theatre 2.

There was stillness at the top end of the operating table, the anaesthetic end. Katty, our on-call consultant anaesthetist, looked over at our hurried actions deep inside the abdomen. A tense expression tightened her usual friendly soft face. There was no more that she and her SpR (specialist registrar) could do at this critical stage of the operation to help us.

That Sunday afternoon, the gods smiled on us. Slowly we gained control of the operative field. I found the left renal vein in the depths of the bloody morass and quickly isolated a segment. We tied off both ends of the vein segment with strong vicryl thread and cut in between, with curved scissors. This manoeuvre exposed the tissue plane containing the critical left renal artery, the leaking tap. With gentle dissection we were able to locate and identify the renal artery and tie it off, before dividing the artery.

At last, the tension that girdled my shoulders eased.

Now we could safely remove the shattered kidney.

Once the kidney had been taken out, we placed fresh large swabs in the operative field, applied firm pressure and waited.

For the first time during the emergency operation, I dared to look up at the multi-coloured squiggles on the LED display of the anaesthetic machine.

'You're doing fine,' Katty said gently, noticing my glance. Those three words were such a gesture of kindness and consideration – a much needed morale boost.

Gingerly, we lifted the swabs.

'Thank God, there's no more bleeding,' Sarah breathed.

The operative field was dry. We checked the tied-off stubs of the left renal artery and vein. They looked secure. Never before had violet (the colour of the vicryl ties) looked so beautiful.

'Let's get the swabs back in,' I said. 'Put some pressure on, and wait a bit to make absolutely sure.'

I looked at Charity.

'Can I have a wide bore tube drain please?' and added,

'Hopefully, we'll be closing soon. Want to do your first count?'

Throughout the ordeal, Charity and her team of theatre nurses had remained calm; exactly the correct instrument had been anticipated, and handed at precisely the right moment – professionalism in the NHS at its demanding best.

On hearing that the first count was correct, I pushed in a tube drain through a small separate stab incision, and quickly fixed it to the skin with a silk stitch. It is tiresome if, once the wound's closed, someone accidentally pulls out the drain before it's been secured, requiring the wound to be reopened just to put the drain back in.

I helped Sarah close up the abdominal incision.

Ian looked in, and on being told that all was well, had gone back to the coffee room.

Later, when I went to check on Emma in the recovery room, I was greeted by the happy faces of Katty and the nurses.

I left the hospital exhausted, but elated. The winter evening was closing in; the sun had slipped over the rooftops leaving a deepening mauve sunset.

As I approached Woldingham, and drove along the winding uphill of Slines Oak Road, dusk was drawing a veil across the green fields and copses of the village. When I got home, the back garden was full of shadows.

My partner Sue wasn't home yet. Sue, the tall, willowy, soft-eyed sister of Bensham 2, ran the urology ward with a personal touch, often pitching in with the student nurses for even the most unappealing of tasks, like emptying catheter bags.

13

That Sunday, she was again working late.

In the murky light outside the rear windows of Grove House, I could just make out a sinuous imprint on the grass ending in the outline of Sue's pet village fox, sitting beside the rhododendron bush like a statue of the jackal-headed Egyptian god Anubis.

I opened the window quietly, and lobbed out some of my ham sandwiches that Sue had left in the fridge. A quicksilver shadowy movement confirmed that dinner had reached its rightful recipient.

*

Like most young people, Emma did well after surgery and went home in a few days.

Two weeks later, she walked into clinic, with her smiling boyfriend. Emma looked well. There was colour in her high cheekbones and lustre in her ash brown hair. Her movements were lithe. The cream blouse and long black skirt that she wore sat well on her.

I said that the pathologists had confirmed that her ruptured left kidney had been "hydronephrotic", a condition she had been born with, where the affected kidney was merely a thin bag of fluid with no substance and little function. That explained why her kidney had shattered from just a playful thump. She had been lucky that her boyfriend hadn't waited to bring her in, and that we had been able to go in and remove the bleeding kidney in time.

Emma listened politely, but with little interest. Her gaze was firmly fixed on her fingertips, studying with intensity the coral pink nail polish.

'Well Emma,' I said. 'I'm happy to say that your blood tests are all fine. You can be discharged now.'

I added with a teasing smile, 'You won't need to see us ever again.'

Her face brightened as she pushed back her chair, she seemed to be in a hurry to get away.

Her boyfriend closed the clinic door with a soft click, mouthing a last silent 'Thank you'.

CHAPTER 2

Appendicectomy

Operating Theatre, Top Floor, John Anderson Casualty
Block (CB Top)
Medical College Hospitals, Calcutta – 1974

1.

A young woman is being anaesthetised in CB Top theatre. She looks small and fragile as she lies on the operating table in her linen hospital smock, her arms bare. The red and white bangles on her thin wrists have been covered up with micropore surgical tape. The bangles, the *shakha* and *pola* made of white conch-shell and red coral, are the traditional symbols of a Hindu married woman. It would be inauspicious to take them off, even for an operation.

The normally more visible mark of her married status – the *sindoor*, a streak of vermillion in the parting of her hair – is also hidden by a grey theatre cap, placed to gather up and tuck away the long black tresses. The cap somehow attenuates her femininity and gives her face a vulnerable, almost childlike innocence.

It has gone past eleven o'clock at night. Downstairs, it is still bedlam in the casualty department. Outside the hospital, the city noises continue unabated. Double-decker buses on the 2B route all the way from Gariahat in South Calcutta rumble along College Street. The ceaseless honk of rheumy taxis, the shouts of the *thelawallas* (cart pullers) and syncopated human voices compete for ascendancy in the noise level. The clammy heat of pre-monsoon June is pushed back by the cool relief of air-conditioning which hums inside the operating theatre.

Night Sister Malabika Sarkar has personally accompanied her patient in the lift to theatres for the emergency appendicectomy.

'Don't be afraid, it'll soon be over,' she says, stroking the young woman's forehead.

Earlier she'd settled the worried husband with a cup of tea and their four-year-old child with a Marie sugar-coated biscuit.

Dr Aziz Mollah, a short, dark-skinned man of choleric disposition with a wispy chin beard, is the duty anaesthetist. He has inserted the endotracheal tube and stands guard at the head end of the operating table, pumping the oxygen bag with his hand while studying the gauges on the anaesthetic machine. Only when he's absolutely satisfied are we, the surgical team, permitted to approach.

Dr Mollah considers all surgeons a nuisance. 'They're so arrogant, always in a hurry, never stop to think if the operation will make a blind bit of difference to the eventual outcome,' he often voices within himself.

The surgical on-call team that trouble him with difficult cases in the dead of night are his especial bête noir.

A grunt indicates his reluctant acquiescence that we may now come up to the patient and begin the operation.

Gowned in sterile white, along with linen cap and face-mask to complete the ensemble, I don the re-used and re-sterilised yellow rubber surgical gloves. Dr Shivaji Bose, our senior resident, is assisting. I dip the skin-cleansing sponge in a sterile pot of antiseptic iodine solution and "prepare" the skin, thoroughly painting the right lower quadrant of the exposed abdomen.

Dr Bose and I then towel off the operative field, leaving a small square of "sterilised" skin exposed. We apply metal towel clips at each corner with care, so as not to catch and damage the skin concealed underneath the green towels.

Standing opposite me on the left hand side of the patient, Dr Shivaji Bose picks up the stainless steel scalpel as it lies glinting under the glare of the ceiling-mounted theatre light. He hands it to me, placing the blunt handle on my outstretched gloved palm, like a benediction. It's his signal to say, 'OK, you can begin.' The implication being that he would swiftly take over if I fumbled, or if difficulties arose that he considered beyond my capabilities as a neophyte, a raw twenty-three-year young intern, aspiring for that first precarious foothold on the surgical ladder.

I start with a small incision centred on McBurney's point. As I draw the scalpel blade across the skin, a thin wake of blood follows. The tissue parts and reveals golden-yellow globules of fat. I discard the skin blade and deepen the incision down to the glistening white sheet that is the external oblique aponeurosis, a tough fibrous layer that adds strength to the abdominal wall.

I pick up diathermy forceps to coagulate the small spurting vessels in the fat, and then insert a Travers self-retaining retractor to keep the wound open.

I make a little nick in the external oblique aponeurosis and extend the cut up and down with McIndoe scissors. My first assistant clips and holds open the two leaves of the divided aponeurosis – now we see the velvety russet-red bundles of the internal oblique and transversus abdominis muscles, beneath which is the peritoneal membrane. I'm handed fine artery forceps, the closed tips of which I gently push in between the plump muscle bundles and then carefully open to create a gap. Dr Bose inserts the blades of two narrow Langenbeck retractors to hold open the space created.

The small space reveals the shining opalescent membrane that is the parietal peritoneum. With fine non-toothed dissecting forceps, I pick up a pinch of peritoneal membrane. With index finger and thumb of the left hand, I check that no underlying loop of bowel has inadvertently been caught up. I apply the tips of artery forceps to this tent of peritoneum. I check again for underlying bowel.

Dr Bose checks too. 'It's fine,' he nods in agreement.

With a small-bladed scalpel, I make a nick in the tented up membrane. The peritoneal cavity is now open.

A small amount of turbid fluid from the inflamed appendix escapes and is quickly sucked away. I extend the peritoneal incision with scissors. Inside, I can see the pinkish-grey bowel with slow ripples of contraction. I use delicate Babcock tissue forceps to grasp the caecum, the pouch-like part of the large intestine to the base of which the appendix is attached. Aided with my left forefinger, I ease the caecum out through the peritoneal opening.

The inflamed appendix follows the caecum, and emerges with a "plop". It resembles an engorged earthworm, crimson with rage at being disturbed in its lair. The tip of the inflamed appendix is ominously dark, almost blue-black, an early sign of incipient gangrene. We have got to it just in time, before the appendix burst.

I snare the appendicular artery within the fatty mesoappendix with a tight ligature. It is now safe to remove the inflamed appendix. My assistant straightens it and holds it up with Babcock forceps, while I tie the base where it joins the caecum. I then clip the base a few millimetres above the tie with artery forceps to prevent spillage of toxic contents as I cut across just below the artery forceps with a small knife, metal grating against metal.

The appendix, with the base clipped and sealed by the artery forceps, along with the contaminated knife are discarded and dropped onto a stainless steel kidney-shaped dish held out by the scrub nurse. The clang of metal denotes a reassuring finality. The stainless steel dish containing the diseased appendix and soiled instruments are removed forthwith from the sterile operating area.

The tied-off residual stump of the appendix is invaginated and buried in the caecal wall with a purse-string chromic catgut suture for further security against the spread of infection.

I close the wound in layers, inserting the last interrupted sutures for the skin using fine 3/0 black silk. A small square of porous gauze dressing is placed and held in position with strips of transpore surgical tape. I confirm the final swab, instrument and needle count with the scrub nurse.

Once Dr Mollah has removed the endotracheal tube

and emitted another grunt, I help transfer the young mother from the operating table onto a waiting trolley, which will take her back to the ward to her waiting husband and sleeping child.

I write up the operation notes standing in a corner of the now empty theatre. I then go out in the heavy stagnant air of the darkened corridor outside CB Top theatres. I pull off my cap to wipe my brow, and undo the strings of the face-mask.

I'm on my own here, with only my thoughts for company.

I punch the night air – I have just done my first appendicectomy – my first ever operation.

A faraway voice startles me. 'Bubu, wake up, it's past seven in the morning.'

I open my eyes and see my mother's face smiling through the mosquito net – I've been dreaming again, the same dream.

How many times have I seen this vivid dream? And every time I've woken up all the more eager and determined to do my first operation.

How many times have I mentally gone over each and every step of the operation, each cut and every clip, all the ties and all the sutures in painful longing detail?

Every corner of the house is full of bits of tied sewing thread, evidence of my incessant practice of one-handed surgical knot-tying – a particularly useful exercise, whereby with the rapid mesmerising, alternate use of fore- and middle finger, along with the apposing action of the same thumb, the surgeon can tie a secure surgical knot with just one hand. The non-dominant hand is out of the operating area, used simply to hold the other end of the suture thread high up and away from the tying action. This ability is particularly useful for tying-off blood vessels in deep cramped spaces, such as inside the chest and pelvic cavity.

My mother has good-naturedly chided me for using up her sewing thread for my one-handed knot-tying practice!

2.

The career choice of surgery had not been an absolute given – I had an open mind during my pre-clinical years. I knew that I wanted to be a specialist, not a general practitioner. With my love of physiology, my initial inclination was towards medicine. The desire to be a surgeon came later.

The revelation struck the very first time I walked into operating theatres. I had just started my first clinical year at the Medical College Hospitals, Calcutta. As a lowly medical student, I'd hesitated before plucking up courage to push open the heavy double-doors of theatres in the Prince of Wales Hospital, expecting any moment to be shouted at.

The scene that confronted me was of concentrated, yet calm activity, centred around a supine form on an operating table.

A high priest, all in sacerdotal white, with bloodied hands, was conducting a ritual. The altar was an open abdomen. Other figures, also in white, crowded around the high priest following his clipped orders and non-verbal instructions. Movements appeared unhurried and deliberate as though the sacrament was being drawn out in exaggerated tardiness. A sharp sound, that of a glass vial being cracked open, startled me. This was immediately followed by a familiar cloying smell – the scrub nurse had just opened a glass pellet containing strands of chromic catgut suture kept sterile in absolute alcohol.

No one gave me even a cursory glance. Emboldened, I crept up nearer to the operating table, only to be transfixed by Professor Asok Banerjee's penetrating gaze – deep brown eyes framed in thick spectacles, the rest of his features obscured by the surgical cap and mask, zoned straight into my pupils.

Merlin, in his present day avatar as Professor Asok Banerjee, indicated that I should come forward, closer to the operative field.

In an unexpectedly gentle voice he said, 'Look, this is the liver. See how the gall bladder is attached to the under surface.'

My eyes followed the Chief Druid's dissecting forceps as he pointed to the warm and supple reddish-brown organ, with the adhering dark-green pear-shaped gall bladder, so different from the cold indurated alum-grey slab that I had recently abandoned in a formalin-reeking dissecting room of the anatomy hall.

That was my moment of epiphany. I wanted to do this – I wanted to be a surgeon.

*

Whilst in my internship year at the Medical College Hospitals, I was to spend twelve months in the various departments of the hospital complex in clinical training, before I could be signed off as a fully qualified doctor and receive my MBBS degree.

I spent every available moment in the operating theatres, observing, assisting and scrubbing up whenever the opportunity came my way.

I scrubbed just to hold a retractor, so that I could be part of the action and to obtain a ringside view of the operation.

I did this even during my general medicine and midwifery attachments. As soon as the day's work was completed in the medical and obstetric wards, I'd scoot off to the John Anderson casualty block where all the emergency operations took place. I stayed back, often sleeping in if the operations went on till late at night.

Although my internship year did not require me to be resident in the hospital, and moreover, there was no available hostel accommodation for interns, I'd succeeded in surmounting this obstacle. The more senior trainees, the hospital's surgical residents lived in a doctor's chummery atop the Eden Hospital for Midwifery. This male abode was a shabby set of rooms perched on the roof, hence the moniker Eden Roof hostel. There were five adjacent rooms along the straight line of a corridor. A single communal shower and toilet and a small gloomy kitchen with an open hearth stood at one end.

Each sparsely furnished room accommodated four beds, placed in the corners. The wooden beds were infested with dry rot and stood on wobbly legs. They had a hard non-sprung, whey-coloured mattress covered with a thin sheet. This austere existence did not dampen our spirits, as we were young and absorbed in exciting work.

I inveigled myself into the middle room where Professor Asok Banerjee's residents, led by Dr Shivaji Bose, hung their clothes and stethoscopes and occasionally caught up on sleep. To their amusement, I pushed in an extra bed in a non-existent space by a piece of geometric jugglery that altered the inner contours of the room from a rectangle to a pentagon. My presumption was accepted with indulgent resignation, especially when I pointed out that five was the auspicious number in Hindu numerology.

My first night in Eden Roof was memorable. This was not due to some extraordinary surgical emergency, but rather something far more humdrum, an ineluctable aspect of living in the lower reaches of city life in Calcutta. I was woken up in the middle of the night with a terrible itch. I turned on the weak bedside table-lamp to discover a teeming army of bedbugs swarming all over the thin sheet covering the mattress. The blighters were fattened on my blood. I didn't get much sleep that night. The next morning, I obtained some termite repellent powder. I liberally sprinkled the lumpy chalk on the mattress, the covering sheet and emaciated single pillow, and in every corner and crevice of the wood joins. The toxic powder exterminated the bed bugs, but also left me with a slight wheeze for several days.

*

By this time, I had ensured that my teachers and senior trainees knew that I was single-minded in my focus on a career in surgery. It was almost an addiction. It helped that in my final year, I had won the gold medal for surgery at Medical College.

I became a fixture in the surgical theatres of the hospital.

Compared to the high voltage of an operating theatre, ward work was a 15-watt lamp. The chores of dressing the wounds of burns victims with orange acriflavine paste, of bandaging smelly purulent tuberculous sores, the laborious writing-up of drug and fluid charts, the twice-daily entries in the clinical notes were all dull, repetitive and boring. This was for humbler folk, lesser mortals who'd remain plodding clinical assistants, certainly not for an ambitious young man with lofty aspirations. Surely, my all-consuming determination and the hours that I put in observing, scrubbing and assisting in the operating theatres must rocket me along a trajectory to the ultimate objective – entry to the most noble of guilds – that of consultant surgeons.

At Medical College, it was convention to allow the exceptional trainee to do an operation in their intern year, assisted by a senior. I had no doubt that this would be me. The surgical procedure traditionally earmarked to signify the trainee's rite of passage was appendicectomy - a common abdominal operation, which in most instances is straightforward and takes fifteen to twenty minutes. The trainee would have seen and assisted in many before being allowed to do one himself.

3.

It was a Friday night towards the end of my internship year. The surgical firm led by Professor Asok Banerjee were on-duty for surgical emergencies. I was on the lookout for a suitable case. I knew that I was ready to do my first appendicectomy. Without it having been said, all the nods and hints indicated that this was the night when I'd get to do my first operation.

In my mind, I was convinced that I'd read all the portents correctly and that everything appeared favourable.

My heightened expectations fevered my mind, such that it wandered into narrow alleys of outlandish contemplation as the night wore on. A stray shard of memory settled on a school-day history lesson on the early Romans and their practice of augury, the art of divining, by reading the entrails of sacrificial sheep.

I reflected that had I been at home, I could have invoked the complicity of Suleiman, the *murgiwalla* (literally chicken-seller). Suleiman, a stocky man in a ruched-up sarong-like *lungi*, bare chest and checked *gamcha* (coarse cotton sweat towel) over his left shoulder, would come to our house every other day to provide farm-fresh poultry. He carried an oversized flat basket on his head like a giant sombrero containing the clucking birds. Invariably, he would stroke his short neat beard while assuring my mother that his chickens were the plumpest, healthiest and tastiest around.

He'd then ascend to the open roof, taking each step slowly due to the mild club foot that made him limp only when he did stairs. Here, in privacy, he'd slaughter the selected fowl, skin the carcass and of course, remove the entrails...

As these zany thoughts flitted across my mind, a boy

of seventeen came in with classical symptoms of acute appendicitis. I personally took charge of the admission and all the pre-operative preparation. I chafed during the obligatory minimum hours of nil by mouth. Finally, when the time arrived, I helped my patient onto a trolley and wheeled him into theatres, waving away the sleepy theatre porter.

Dr Shivaji Bose had just finished repairing a strangulated hernia. He was in equable mood. Tiny beads of perspiration softened the bristles of the moustache on his flushed handsome face. He wrote up the op notes while unfastening the top tie of his mask with his free hand. The face-mask dangled insouciantly below his neck, accentuating a rakish appearance.

Nothing was said while we waited for the boy to be anaesthetised by the very same Dr Mollah, now in much worse mood.

'What? Another case? I haven't even had a cup of tea since the last one,' he grumbled aloud.

My fellow intern Swapan was also standing around in theatres. He might be asked to scrub and assist me. Swapan had no interest in being a surgeon. After acquiring his MBBS degree, he would return to his native Birbhum district in North Bengal, far away from the metropolis of Calcutta, to join his father's small-town general practice.

As I saw Dr Mollah slip in the endotracheal tube, I made to go to the hand-wash troughs. Dr Shivaji Bose's sharp voice halted my steps.

'Swapan, go and scrub, you're doing this appendicectomy. I'll assist you.'

Swapan looked at us both in astonishment.

Dr Bose's hard voice broke the heavy silence.

In trenchant tone, he added, 'Gautam, you'll go back to the ward in Prince of Wales, and finish the wound dressings that you left when you came to theatres.'

I could feel the bile at the back of my throat. My mind turned into a whirligig of emotion from bitter disappointment. I turned away before I said something that I'd later come to regret.

Yet my ordeal was not over.

'Gautam, before you go to PWH, you'll scrub with us, you'll hand the swabs and instruments.'

The stakes had been piled even higher. What I was being ordered to do was the job of a mere scrub nurse. My brain formed the words of angry remonstrance; Dr Bose's steely look stilled them dead.

4.

Later when the hurt had partly settled and the pain dulled, my elders and betters took me to our favourite teashop in College Street, just outside the hospital's main entrance.

We sat at a Formica-topped corner table. Rickety chairs were drawn up close to mine, and in the huddle, arms were placed around my shoulders.

I was told, 'Listen Gautam, surgery is more than just operating.'

I keenly studied the tessellated pattern on the chipped Formica tabletop.

'You *have* to give attention to patients, before and after the operation.'

Tea arrived in steaming clay cups, a strong Assam brew laden with milk and heaped with sugar as though to sweeten the harsh lesson.

Dr Shivaji Bose consoled, 'You do have a good pair of hands Gautam, but as a surgeon, you're more than just a technician.'

Dr Bose wiped a smudge of milky tea from his moustache with the heel of his hand. 'Good surgeons always involve themselves in every detail of their patient's care.'

Years later, I would hear similar words of wisdom – 'A good surgeon is an operating physician.'

I felt a pleasurable weight under the table. It was Mithu, the teashop's black and white cat, her curved back rubbing against my leg in sympathy.

At this stage, *shingaras* were ordered with more cups of tea. The classical Bengali *shingara* is not an attenuated triangular samosa. This is a ziggurat of a samosa, a tetrahedron of crisp flaky filo pastry packed with spicy potato, peas and roasted peanuts. It is served piping hot. You bring it to your mouth, holding the corners with fingertips, and then after the first bite, drop it on your plate as steam escapes along with the tantalising aroma of fenugreek, cumin and red chillies.

A few weeks after this, I did get to do my first appendicectomy, supervised and assisted by... yes, the very same Dr Shivaji Bose.

*

Four years later, after I had attained my Master of Surgery from the University of Calcutta, it would be Shivajida (in Bengali language and culture, the appellation *da* to a man's first name confers an equal measure of respect and warmth to an individual who is a little older) and his caring, doe-eyed wife, Rupali, who would come to receive me, as I emerged, jet-lagged and spatially uncertain, into the Arrivals concourse of Heathrow Airport Terminal 3.

They'd take me in their second-hand car, a two-door yellow Datsun, to their hospital accommodation after a brief stop for food supplies at the Brent Cross shopping centre.

I would be welcomed into their modest two-bedroom apartment in the doctor's quarters of Whipps Cross Hospital in East London and eased into my new life as an NHS junior doctor – far away from home in my city of Calcutta, from my mother, my father, young wife and two little children.

CHAPTER 3

Reculer Pour Mieux Sauter – taking a step back to make a better throw

Medical College Hospitals, Calcutta – 1970s
Newmarket General Hospital – 1983

Rajib Bindu Chatterjee MS, FRCS (England and Edinburgh), known out of earshot as RBC, was a much-admired Professor-Director of Surgery at the Medical College, Calcutta. Secretly, he quite liked the sobriquet RBC, with its implied longevity. (Red blood cells swirl in our peripheral blood for an impressive 120 days, dwarfing the miserly few days of compatriot white blood cells.)

There were many aphorisms attributed to the great man, tall and stooped, who was a skilled general surgeon as well as a great clinical teacher.

The one I liked most was, 'To be a good surgeon, one must also be an astute tactician.'

Professor Chatterjee would explain to the attentive medical students gathered in the tiered rows of the grand lecture theatre of the Medical College, Calcutta that most operations, especially planned elective ones, had a defined and pre-determined sequence of steps. Yet each operation was uniquely different with the additional potential of surprising the surgeon with the unsuspected googly.

The professor taught that it was therefore essential for an aspiring surgeon to develop a flexible mind-set, such that when confronted with the unforeseen, he had the nous and the presence of mind to deal effectively with the new situation. Often this would involve a strategic and careful withdrawal.

Just as the battlefield commander perforce must be a master of strategy, so too with the practising surgeon. Like the general who orders a tactical retreat when faced with *force majeure* so that he can come back and fight another day, so too must the good surgeon learn the importance of *reculer pour mieux sauter*.

*

In the summer of 1983, I was doing a two-week locum as Registrar in General Surgery at Newmarket General Hospital. Locum jobs are traditionally frowned upon as they do not look good on a trainee's CV. They give the impression of impermanence and raise the suspicion of inability to secure a substantive appointment. There are exceptions of course, as with my circumstances that year.

*

In 1983, I was already in a substantive training post at the Huddersfield Royal Infirmary, West Yorkshire. I was working in the pathology laboratory as research registrar on a project investigating the role of blood group antigens in bladder cancer.

I wanted to do the locum job in Newmarket, using a

portion of my annual leave, in order to supplement my junior doctor's salary. As it were, pure research jobs paid relatively less, compared to clinical posts that had inherent additional emoluments for being on-call. Moreover, it was an excellent opportunity to keep up clinical and operating skills, as well as for my wife and young children to experience another beautiful part of England.

We loved going to Newmarket and exploring the Suffolk countryside. We discovered a genteel milieu in Newmarket town. There was also the advantage of proximity to both Ely and Cambridge.

Ely Cathedral, a beacon amidst the surrounding flat fenlands, drew visitors like a powerful magnet with its majestic spires and harmonious blend of Romanesque, Gothic and Norman styles of architecture. It's a shame that most of the stained glass and sculpture have been lost as a result of the depredations of the Dissolution during Henry Tudor's time.

Another must for us was Evensong at King's College Chapel, especially when the full choir was in performance. It was an experience, almost sensual, that could only be fully appreciated by actual presence. Once inside the chapel, it was easy to shut one's mind to the outside world, the sordid and discordant, and be absorbed in the stirring choral notes of 'Miserere, Mei Deus' soaring up to the magnificent vaulted ceiling of the chapel.

*

Newmarket General Hospital with its spread-out single-storey buildings, cosy junior doctor's mess with a real fireplace and comfy armchairs, and overall unhurried atmosphere was so different from the frenetic whirl of bigger hospitals. It was a friendly place in which to work. Moreover, I got on well with my chief there.

Mr Robin Taggart FRCS had the bearing of a field marshal. He was a senior consultant of the old school with a direct, no-nonsense approach. This man was an experienced general surgeon and an inspiring teacher. Although firm in his dealings, he was also fair and possessed that unique ability to command respect from his juniors without the need to instil fear.

I had an operating list on my very first day. I started off with a straightforward stripping and ligation of varicose veins. The next patient on the table was a middle-aged man with a recurrent groin hernia.

Operating on hernia recurrences is always more awkward. There is scarring from the previous surgery which makes it much more difficult to accurately identify tissue planes, thus increasing the risk of inadvertently cutting important nearby structures, in this case, the vas deferens and the testicular artery.

I had just succeeded in teasing the hernia sac from the fibrous scar tissue, when I heard a gravelly voice over my shoulder. 'Hmm, you seem to be getting on all right.'

As I recognised the boss's voice and took a step back, Mr Taggart said, 'It's OK lad, you're doing fine here, carry on,' and left the operating theatre.

I later learned from the consultant anaesthetist that Mr Taggart had said in his laconic style, 'That young locum fellow seems to have a good pair of hands.'

During the second week of my locum period, I was

on-call most nights. One evening hadn't been particularly busy, just a couple of abscesses that required incision and drainage. Shortly before midnight, the senior house officer in accident & emergency called through.

'We've got a seventeen-year-old girl with a two-day history of right lower abdo pain. We think its appendicitis.'

'OK, I'll see her, be down right away.'

As I pulled open the curtains of the bay in the emergency department, I found a pale, skinny girl in tears. She was sitting up on the A&E trolley holding a grey cardboard sick bowl in one hand, her other clutching onto her mother's arm.

I checked her name on the clipboard and also noted that she was running a temperature and that her pulse rate was fast.

'Hi Jessica, I'm Gautam, surgical registrar. Need to ask you a couple of quick questions and then have a little feel of your tummy... is that OK?'

She nodded, her eyes brimming with tears.

I took a succinct history. Jessica also confirmed that her periods were regular and that she had finished one two weeks ago - this was important, as in the 1980s, ultrasound was not that readily available. The last thing I wanted was to open her up and find a life-threatening ruptured ectopic pregnancy, with the gynae registrar unavailable, scrubbed up with another case.

I needed to feel Jessica's abdomen, especially to check whether she was tender over McBurney's point.

Normally, the appendix is tucked away deep inside the right lower quadrant of the abdominal cavity. In most people, there is a specific surface point under which it tends to lie. Pressing down on this eponymous point elicits sharp pain if the appendix is inflamed.

To find McBurney's point one needs to trace a fingertip from the belly-button diagonally downwards and to the right, towards the anterior superior iliac spine, the bony spur that you feel just under the tip of the middle finger if you were to stand with hands on hips, as though squaring off to an imaginary adversary! Two-thirds of the way from the umbilicus down to the anterior superior iliac spine, one reaches McBurney's point. This landmark is also of importance when we operate as the skin incision for appendicectomy is centred on McBurney's point.

Jessica flinched as I tried to put a hand on her tummy. Just fingertip pressure over McBurney's point was excruciatingly painful. She violently pushed my hand away and wept, shaking her head despite her mother clasping her hand and stroking her hair.

The overall clinical picture was clearly that of acute appendicitis. Emergency appendicectomy had to be performed. I rang through from A&E to alert the duty anaesthetist and theatres.

Jessica was transferred to the surgical ward. In a while, she would be wheeled into the anaesthetic room of the emergency theatre.

*

The house officer on-call with me that night was looking forward to scrubbing up for the operation. Roger, a dapper rowing blue who'd qualified with distinction from Cambridge, was leaning towards a surgical career.

'Gautam, are you happy to take me through this one?' meaning that he wanted to do the operation, with me guiding and assisting him. It would be his first ever appendicectomy.

Remembering my own eagerness to do my very first appendicectomy at the Medical College, Calcutta, I said, keeping a straight face, 'Sure, but it'll cost you!'

To sweeten the deal, Roger quickly added, 'I'll buy the pints tomorrow when we're both off-duty.'

We walked to theatres with Ruth, the medical student who'd stayed up to observe the emergency appendicectomy. The three of us stood in our blue scrubs in the emergency operating room chatting with the young theatre nurse setting up her instrument trolley. Eurythmics belted out from a portable transistor radio in a corner of the operating theatre.

Earlier, I had asked the anaesthetist to alert me once our patient, Jessica, had been anaesthetised, and before she was moved to the actual operating room.

A short while later, there was a knock on the connecting door indicating that we could enter the anaesthetic area.

I went inside the cramped anaesthetic room and checked with the anaesthetist whether it was all right for me to re-examine the abdomen. My thinking was that I'd now be better able to palpate, as with the effect of the muscle relaxant injected as part of the anaesthetic cocktail, the abdominal muscles would no longer be rigid; and of course being under anaesthetic, she would feel no pain.

On lifting the patterned blue and white cotton gown to expose the abdomen, I could clearly see, just above the upper edge of the hospital issue briefs, a faint though distinct swelling in the lower right abdomen. It looked like a slight elevation in the hollow of her pale abdomen. As I placed the palm of my right hand to palpate, I could easily feel a firm lump, like a little hillock on the flat of her belly.

I knew immediately that this was an appendix mass.

The scenario had changed.

An appendix mass forms when inflammation from the infected appendix spreads to the adjoining bowel segment. It is also entangled by the omentum, which is a stippled fatty apron that covers the internal abdominal organs and works as a protective barrier in situations such as this, to wall off and contain further spread of the infection.

Such a mass is an inseparable hard coagulum of the inflamed appendix, the nearby bowel, and omentum.

In this situation, operating is foolhardy. One would do more harm than good. The tissue planes would be blurred. Trying to dissect out the appendix from this cemented mass would be an operative nightmare and a recipe for disaster, as we would be running the risk of perforating the adherent loops of small and large intestine.

The sensible thing here is to be resolute and have the courage to abandon the operation, and to explain the reasons for so doing to the anaesthetist, the assistants and the theatre nurses, and later on, the patient and her family.

The treatment plan now changes over from surgery to the use of a combination of powerful antibiotics and intravenous fluids.

With this non-operative or "conservative" management, the infection settles and a few weeks later, one can go back in, and safely remove the now quiescent appendix that is no longer red-hot, and moreover, has loosened itself from the grip of adjoining organs.

The house officer, Roger, quickly overcame his disappointment of not doing his first ever appendicectomy that evening. The medical student Ruth was happy to have learnt a valuable lesson.

*

The next morning, Mr Taggart was leading his customary ward round. I was at his side as the firm's registrar along with rest of the entourage of senior house officer, house officers, a bevy of Cambridge University medical students and the surgical ward sister.

I presented the emergency case of the night before with the surgical team crowded around Jessica's bed.

Mr Taggart listened quietly without a flicker of expression on his face, his head ever so slightly inclined. He waited patiently till I had finished speaking. Then, taking his time, he turned his back to me and addressed his troops. His brow was furrowed and there was a set line to his thin lips.

In a disquieting, low voice, he said, 'This young girl comes in seriously ill, with obvious acute appendicitis, this locum chap from Yorkshire takes her to theatres, and then...'

There was an ominous pause. 'Doesn't do the operation!'

Like an experienced stage performer, he allowed the portent of his words to sink in.

'What do you think I should do with this fellow?'

There was a stunned silence. Everyone was convinced that I was in for a roasting. Only I could sense the twinkle in his eye.

With an almost theatrical flourish, Robin Taggart turned back on his heels, looked straight at me and said with a smile, 'I would pat him on the back... for taking absolutely the right decision.'

In fact, he followed that up with a hearty thump.

*

Jessica herself was feeling much better. The antibiotics and crystalline fluids poured into her veins overnight had worked their magic. She was clear-eyed and no longer in pain. She even permitted a gentle examination, and this time, did not wince when I placed my hand on her tummy.

A few weeks later, when the inflammation had settled, and I'd gone back to Huddersfield and to my lab, Robin Taggart uneventfully took out Jessica's appendix, so that it could never again be a source of trouble.

The subsequent silvery hairline scar centred on McBurney's point was hardly visible.

CHAPTER 4

The Kidney Transplant and the Dropped Stent

Guy's Hospital – 1984

It was three o'clock in the morning and I was doing a kidney transplant in Theatre 5 at Guy's Hospital.

The donor kidney had been retrieved from a young man on a motorbike, involved in a head-on collision on a winding Hampshire country road, at dawn the day before. Tragically, he had succumbed to his appalling injuries despite being resuscitated at the roadside and thereafter airlifted to hospital. The young man carried a donor card, which permitted the regional transplant team to harvest his organs.

The donor kidney had arrived at reception in Guy's Tower, just after midnight in a sterile container within a sealed box packed with ice slush. My senior consultant, Mick, had called through to my on-call room in Elizabeth Newcomen House, situated just outside the main hospital precinct. Mick and his colleague Chris were the two consultant surgeons at the South-East England Regional Renal Transplant Unit based at Guy's Hospital, and were also my training supervisors. I was the surgical registrar in my second year in renal transplant surgical training.

Over the last twelve months, Mick and Chris

had supervised me through many kidney transplant operations. Mick was happy for me to go ahead with the operation that night, and would be available to come in if needed.

The transplant co-ordinators had identified from our waiting list the person whose tissue-typing results best matched those of the donor. She was alerted by the pager specially provided by the renal unit. Along with her husband, Joanne was on her way to Guy's.

Through the hospital's switchboard, quiet of normal chatter at this late hour, I made just the one telephone call.

My call alerted a single senior medical student, a keen German girl, spending a secondment year at Guy's from Cologne University. She went by the name of Beatta, a languorously stretched out Bee-aa-ta. Her surname was Baier. Whenever she said her full name, there was always a slight but perceptible pause between first and surname, as though she was permitting the listener time to allow the complexity of her christian name to sink in.

Beatta in turn roused three other medical students. All four would have their allocated tasks. Two would go to Astley Cooper ward to ensure that all the necessary pre-operative preparations for the recipient were in place prior to my own final check. The other two would go straight to theatres in Guy's Tower and would later scrub with me to assist for the transplant operation.

*

I went to the ward and shook hands with Joanne, a forty-one-year-old mother of two, and her husband David who

43

worked as a joiner in Southwark. Joanne was severely diabetic. The disease had started in early childhood. Insulin injections had been an unshakeable part of her growing up. Two years ago, her kidneys failed from the assault of this particularly resistant form of the disease. Hence the term "brittle diabetes". She had to be placed on kidney dialysis.

Three days a week, Joanne was hooked up to the dialysis machine by tubes taking blood away from her body, and bringing it back to her after being cleansed. She was incarcerated in the dialysis room for several hours, chained to this clicking flashing impersonal appliance which kept her alive, yet from whose grasp she sought release.

Three whole days every week, the family's priorities shifted from school runs, music lessons, and netball practice.

Then there was the tiredness, a perpetual draining lethargy that seeped into her mind and required determination to overcome.

Joanne and her family were elated; at last a match had come up. They hoped the transplant would work, and the family would get back the cherished mother and wife of happier days, restored to health and energy.

*

In Theatre 5 of Guy's Tower, Sally, the anaesthetic senior registrar was chatting with the night theatre staff and the medical students. She'd already drawn up the anaesthetic cocktails.

My first task in theatres was to take the donor kidney out of the box and prepare the organ for transplantation into the recipient. I sat down before a trolley covered with a sterile towel, on which rested a plastic bowl containing a clear electrolyte solution. With great care, I placed the precious donor organ in this bath. I trimmed off excess fatty tissue with fine scissors and checked the blood vessels with a delicate probe to ensure patency and absence of leaks. The ureter, which is the 25 cm worm-like tube, down which urine travels from the kidney, was similarly checked.

The kidney felt cold. It looked grey and lifeless. Yet locked inside its delicate architecture, this precious organ held the potential of saving the life of a human being.

Voices and sounds in the adjoining anaesthetic room alerted me that Joanne had been brought down from the ward. Soon she was anaesthetised, and wheeled into the operating room.

Through a 6-inch incision just above the right groin, I dissected down to create a space where the transplanted kidney would find a new home. The external iliac artery and vein, to which would be attached the artery and vein of the transplant kidney, were identified and cleared of covering fat and fascia.

The delicate vascular anastomosis to join together the blood vessels required suture material of double-ended 6/0 monofilament nylon. With surgical suture material, the higher the first number, the finer it is. Most routine general surgical operations do not go higher than 3/0. Hence, 6/0 is exquisitely slender – an arm's length of the finest baby hair, a cerulean-blue slippery filament seamlessly attached at each end to a tiny silver crescent of needle, hence the surgical term "double ended".

This is the most intense part of the operation. The vascular anastomosis has to be perfect. One cannot have leaks and it absolutely must not be under tension. Without a good blood supply, the kidney will die and the transplant operation fail.

As I took off the vascular clamps after inserting the last stitch and tying the last knot, fresh warm blood, rich in oxygen, pumped out from Joanne's eager heart, waiting impatiently, held back by the clamps, surged into the donor kidney filling its arterioles and capillaries. In an instant, the kidney changed colour. From dull pewter, it was transformed to a glowing healthy pink. It was as though the transplanted kidney had blushed with pleasure at being brought back to life.

Everyone in theatres, including Sally who had seen it all before, smiled. It was akin to a childbirth.

The rest of the operation was relatively less taxing, yet required skill and attention to detail. I joined the ureter of the donor kidney to Joanne's urinary bladder by cutting open the bladder, making a small nick in the inner lining near the dome, then pulling in the lower end of the ureter through this nick and stitching it in.

I now required a special ureteric stent to splint the ureter-bladder anastomosis that I'd just fashioned.

*

A ureteric stent is a slim and supple polyurethane tube extensively used in urology. The principle is similar to that in cardiology, where the interventional cardiologist skilfully negotiates the coronary artery and positions a cardiac stent to open up an occluded artery. Lifesaving oxygen-rich blood can now reanimate the ischaemic heart.

In urology, ureteric stents help us open up ureters obstructed by a tumour or a stone. Stents also assist us when we repair a damaged ureter, by acting as a temporary splint while healing takes place.

All ureteric stents have a self-retaining curl at each end to avert dislodgement. The curl at the top end stops the stent from slipping down into the bladder, while the bottom curl thwarts upward migration into the kidney. The curls are denoted pigtails – the tight circles conjure up the rear of a scampering piglet!

The manufacture of ureteric stents with memory-retentive pigtails is an exemplar of cutting edge co-polymer technology. Stents are indispensable articles of every modern urologist's tool kit.

*

Our scrub nurse Sister Cecilia Lim had already taken out a stent from the sterile cellophane packaging. I'd been concentrating with such intensity, whilst inserting every single tiny vascular stitch to join the blood vessels, that I hadn't heard the sharp tearing of the cellophane wrapper being ripped open. Cecilia had dipped the blue stent in a bath of sterile water in a plastic dish, where it floated contentedly. Stents have a hydrophilic surface coating, which on contact with water make them slippery and easier to insert.

I was now on the home run, the tension had eased from my shoulder and neck muscles. I even joined in the frisson of conversation and good-humoured banter. I asked for the ureteric stent, and Sister Lim brought the dish near my reach. I picked up the worm-like tube, wet and slippery.

As I transferred the stent to the operative field, it slipped from my gloved hand and slithered down the side of the sterile drapes towards the small space between the instrument trolley and the towelled operative area.

Tim, my alert first assistant, and I, both made a lunge. To our chagrin, the pesky tube eluded us both and stubbornly fell on the theatre floor.

(Accidentally dropping instruments in theatre, though undesirable, is not rare. When it does happen, it is critically important that everyone has recognised the fact, so that there is no panic at the end of the operation, when the swab, needle and instrument count is tallied and matched up.)

No one reproved my inadvertent yet clumsy slip. Sister Lim, seated on a stool on the opposite side of the operating table, looked up at the theatre runner and simply asked her to get another stent.

While waiting the few minutes that it took the runner to go next door to stores for a fresh package, a thought crossed my mind.

'By the way, out of interest, how much does one of these stents cost?' I asked Sister Lim.

'About eighty-five pounds,' she replied.

I was shocked into silence.

This was 1984.

It was just four years since I'd arrived in Britain from India. Eighty-five pounds sterling was nearly 10,000 rupees. My father had recently retired as a senior London-qualified chartered accountant in the venerable Calcutta firm of Lovelock and Lewes. His final month's pay cheque was written out for 2,000 rupees!

Back home in Calcutta, at the Medical College Hospitals, we junior doctors would accept the generosity and friendship of medical representatives of various pharmaceutical companies. As a tribe, the medical reps were smart young men who came to the hospital on noisy brilliantly polished Royal Enfield motorcycles. We took freebies from the reps because they were not free ball-point pens and sticky notepads. *We took the gifts because they were prized physician's samples of life-saving medicines.*

Drugs were costly in the India of the 1970s. The government hospitals could only provide basic medicines. The patients themselves and their relatives had to pay for expensive injections like powerful antibiotics, even blood for transfusion. People coming to state-run hospitals were poor to a depth unimaginable in the Western world. Only the rich, a microscopic percentage of the massive population, could afford private clinics.

We had no welfare state in India. There was no safety net, like the United Kingdom's NHS, free at the point of delivery, free at the point of care.

I, like my other junior doctor chums at the Medical College Hospitals, Calcutta, would hoard the free sachets, packages and vials in rusty wobbly steel cabinets in our doctor's changing rooms. Gentamicin, a then newly discovered antibiotic that saved lives in cases of overwhelming sepsis, was as keenly cherished and squirrelled away as the gold offered by Hindu devotees and secreted in the underground vaults of India's age-old temples.

We used these treasured free medical samples sparingly for patients in the general wards, who had no means to afford expensive drugs.

*

At the end of that night in Guy's, I felt elated. I'd done the kidney transplant without having to call in the boss.

Yet my conscience was niggled by the unnecessary wastage of, at least to me, an expensive piece of theatre kit.

It was almost as though I had failed to show proper respect to the NHS and to the taxpayers who funded this amazing institution founded on an ethical principle, so elegant in its simplicity and truth - care should be available at the time of need for everyone, prince or pauper.

*

Next morning, I found Joanne sitting up enjoying a cup of weak tea. She looked fresh and her smile was no longer tinged with the wan tiredness of before.

The rest of her post-operative recovery was uneventful. The new kidney picked up speed straightaway. Although she would be on powerful immune-suppressant drugs for the rest of her life to prevent her body from rejecting the transplant, she was delighted at the thought of never having to go back to a dialysis machine.

I went to Astley Cooper ward to say goodbye the day Joanne was due to leave hospital. Her freckled six-year old daughter Millie was sitting on the bed beside her.

I shook hands with a smiling Joanne.

'Look Millie,' she said. 'This is the nice doctor who gave me my new kidney. Say "hello".'

'Hello doctor,' Millie said, shyly pulling at her pigtails. 'Thank you for Mummy's new kidney.'

The dropped stent no longer seemed important.

CHAPTER 5

Amelia

Woldingham, Surrey – 1990
Guy's Hospital – 1984

In 1990, I completed higher surgical training and was appointed consultant urological surgeon to the Mayday Hospital, now known as Croydon University Hospital.

With our school-going son and daughter, two Labrador crosses and five cats, my first wife Baidehi and I commenced house-hunting in Surrey. We chose to live in the village of Woldingham where an old Victorian house entwined in ivy, with high privet hedges, took us in and enfolded us in warmth.

Having endured cramped hospital accommodation for most of the nine years of my training, we eagerly sent around our new calling card – *Grove House, High Drive, Woldingham, Surrey*. It had a better ring to it than Flat 46, Third Floor, Doctors' Quarters, Sudbury Royal Infirmary.

A short walk from our house was the Glebe with cricket field, clubhouse and outdoor tennis courts. On nearby Station Road were the village hall and the medieval style St Paul's parish church, built of flint and stone.

Life in Woldingham unlocked open-air opportunities not readily available in the urban conurbation of Croydon. There was the Haliloo Valley Golf Club, where I never got to hit a ball, but gave many an evening talk on prostate problems to silver-haired Rotarians. There were two mega garden centres at each end of the village.

We also had the Woldingham Equestrian Centre, located just off Slines Oak Road, which looped through the village.

Horse-riding was popular in Woldingham. Several of the nearby farms had well-stocked stables and paddocks. We were mindful whilst driving in the village – horses had right of way. We slowed down at crossings and smiled to acknowledge the nod of a passing riding-hat.

One day after coming home from school, my thirteen-year-old daughter Meenakshi asked, 'Dad, can I take up horse riding? Becks and Danielle have been doing it for a year and really love it.'

I stared at my daughter's face. Dread numbed my mind as her eager words tumbled out. My thoughts fled the room and raced back seven years, tearing past countless images.

The tachometer needle juddered to a stop at one face.

'Dad, what *are* you thinking of?'

'Darling, let's see how your ma feels,' I said, trying to parry.

Meenakshi had been named by her doting grandparents after a Hindu goddess of exquisite beauty. Our daughter had inherited the honey and ivory complexion and the delicate features of my mother. At home, we called her by her pet name – Munni ("adored little girl" in the Bengali of Calcutta).

I mentioned the horse-riding to my wife when she came home that evening. Baidehi had always been able to take practical decisions with minimum fuss.

'Of course she must,' she said. 'It'll be good for Munni to pick up a new proficiency. She'll make new friends. Also, think of all that fresh air and exercise.'

*

That weekend, I went with Meenakshi to visit the equestrian centre on a cloudless spring day with a mild westerly breeze. We met the instructor Jacqui, a tall, rangy woman in her early thirties. She talked to us animatedly, gesturing with her hands and arms in enthusiastic encouragement. The grooms, many of whom were teenagers themselves, were equally warm and friendly. Jacqui introduced Meenakshi to her new friend – her mount, a glossy palomino chestnut stallion endearingly named Churchill.

As I walked home with Meenakshi in the spring sunshine, my mind once again went back to that face of yesteryear – that of Amelia.

Seven years earlier, during my training period, I had just started a new job, working as surgical registrar in the renal transplant unit at Guy's Hospital.

My senior trainer Mick was a superb surgeon with vast experience. A man of great personal charm, he possessed an easy-going manner that smoothed his way in unfamiliar operating theatres. (A transplant surgeon's job requires him to work in the operating theatres of several hospitals other than his own base hospital, to retrieve cadaveric kidneys from brain dead donors.)

With his first joke, often risqué, Mick could instantaneously disarm prickly personalities and inveigle himself to an unfamiliar theatre team as though he were a regular who had just popped in to do yet another routine operation.

Only *he* had the chutzpah to saunter into theatre and say, 'Arlene luvvie, I know you're meant to have finished at five... but I *know* you're going to stay back for this retrieval,' and get away with it.

When we were on-call over the weekend (I was on-call every other weekend, while Mick, a workaholic insomniac, was perpetually on-call), he would ring on Saturday at five in the morning and say, 'All set squire? We'd better go round the patch.'

The 'patch' that he alluded to was the entire south-east of England with Guy's as the nodal point for kidney transplantation.

From Brighton to Dungeness, from Basingstoke to Worthing, we criss-crossed the home counties checking on transplant patients and satellite dialysis units.

One of our tasks whilst on-call was to retrieve cadaver kidneys. This was a surgical chore that I had as yet not reconciled to. New to the field of transplant surgery, I retained that residue of unease towards organ removal from a dead human being, a brain-dead person. I did not experience the same disquiet with living donors.

Cadaveric organ retrieval was to me somewhat morbid. There was something saturnine about the whole thing.

*

In live donor surgery, the kidney is surgically removed through a 6-inch cut in the loin. Adequate lengths of renal artery and vein are taken so as not to struggle when it comes to sewing the transplanted kidney's blood vessels to those of the recipient.

It is equally important to ensure that the donor does not come to harm from the nephrectomy. We protect the donor's aorta and inferior vena cava of which the artery and vein of the excised kidney are branches. The loin wound is meticulously closed in layers to prevent future wound hernia.

Like a connoisseur taking out a precious *objet d'art* from his treasured art collection, we pay equal, meticulous attention to what is taken as well as to what remains.

With cadaveric retrievals on the other hand, we can remove segments of the aorta and vena cava with impunity in order to obtain the best lengths of renal artery and vein; and the wound can be closed in one time-saving layer.

Moreover, the incision itself is different.

In live donor surgery, the loin incision is of just sufficient length to perform the retrieval nephrectomy safely. Nowadays, this is done by keyhole surgery.

In cadaveric surgery, given that we are removing both the kidneys and someone else is taking out the heart, lungs and liver, a sweeping slice starting from the top of the sternum, the breastbone, extending right down to the pubis is used – likened in ghoulish comparison to a mortuary incision.

*

Mick, with his long years as a senior transplant surgeon, seemed inured to such qualms. He carried, in the boot of his sporty blood-red Ford Sierra with its flared tail-fin, a full set of sterile instruments and kidney preservative kit, just in case a call about a donor came through while he was on the road.

Suitable donor organs were few and far between and we had a long list of potential recipients on dialysis machines whose lives would be immeasurably improved by a successful kidney transplant.

That chill autumn morning of early November 1984 was my second Saturday on-call working with Mick.

As soon as I had put the phone down after answering his 5am call, I hurriedly dressed in my tiny hospital room at Elizabeth Newcomen House in Guy's, discarding the tie that was de rigeur in the wards. When Mick tooted outside in the pre-dawn dark, I fleet-footed downstairs, jumped in and strapped on the seat belt. The engine had been idling less than a minute.

As was his wont, Mick hit the accelerator no sooner than I had shut the passenger door, and we tore off towards our destination – Brighton, our largest satellite unit.

By mid-morning we'd finished the ward round at Brighton General and were back on the road, when Mick's pager buzzed.

He took one hand off the steering wheel to pull the pager out from the holster clipped to his trouser belt and looked at the display. His face brightened, as he said, 'Little detour Gautam, a donor's just come up in Hastings.'

We got off the A23 at Patcham and took the A27 towards Hastings and what was to be my first cadaveric kidney retrieval.

With Mick's disdain for speed constraints, we soon

pulled up at the front entrance of the Conquest Hospital in St Leonard's-on-Sea.

Inside the main lobby of the hospital, sign-post arrows sped us towards intensive care. I tried to keep pace with the boss whilst carrying the large wrapped retrieval surgery toolkit under my arm.

We swung open the double doors of ICU and were greeted by the duty consultant. She told us that a horse-rider had been thrown off and sustained a non-survivable head injury.

Brain stem tests had confirmed brain death.

She pointed towards a bed in the far corner of ICU next to a large window.

Mick and I walked with the ICU consultant, towards our potential cadaveric donor. I stood at the foot of the bed and gazed at the beautiful face of a thirteen-year-old girl. She wore the blue and white hospital smock that reached up to the hollow of her neck. Her white arms were bare; a single intravenous fluid line connected her forearm to an infusion bag hanging from a nearby drip stand. The adjoining ventilator machine breathed for her through an endotracheal tube.

'Such a shame... she's so young,' Dr Elizabeth Mearns, consultant intensivist said. 'She was even wearing a riding hat.'

As we gazed, a slanting shaft of sunlight fell through the window on the girl's arm. The rays lit up a square of skin where the fine golden down glowed against the dull buff of the cannula plaster.

The electrocardiograph squiggle showed a strong healthy heartbeat.

Her innocent face was in repose with no sign of distress. She had that peaceful look which a happy dream brings.

The rosy hue of her oval face set off the rich tones of her amber-blonde hair. Her lips were red, her fingertips and ear lobes warm to my touch.

Yet she was brain dead.

Amelia's eyelids were closed.

I could sense the soft hazel eyes. I imagined eyes that were enquiring, fearless and joyful, that looked upon kittens with love, and gazed to the future with hope and confidence.

Mick woke me from my reverie. 'Come on Gautam, we've got to go and speak to the parents.'

A nurse led us to an annexe room.

'The father's in there,' she whispered. 'Mum had to be taken home. She broke down when Dr Mearns brought up organ donation.'

In the family room, standing with his back to us, was a tall, strongly built man with dark brown hair, wearing a faded Barbour jacket with elbow patches. He stood at a window, looking out towards distant fields. There was an untouched cup of tea on a saucer at a side table.

Amelia's father Richard shook hands with us. His face betrayed no emotion. When he spoke, there was no trace of the plaintive in his voice. That would come later. The grief of extreme loss would overwhelm at times of weakness, it would steal up and strike at the unexpected moment, like a stalking footpad.

Richard said that the morning had started out no different from other weekends.

'We live on a farm with a paddock. She's been riding from when she was small.'

A pause, then he added, 'Amelia always made sure she wore her riding hat.'

Richard knew why Mick and I were there.

'Yes, I'm certain,' he said. 'She'd have wanted to give her organs.' He thought for a moment. 'She was gentle with all the farm animals, kind with everyone she knew.' A phone rang on a wall-extension in the room. We ignored the intrusion and waited for it to cease. 'Yes, I'm sure she would've wanted to help others.'

Normally, I enjoy operating. But as we transgressed Amelia's young, perfect body, this was one operation that I wished not to be a part of. Of course, I didn't betray my feelings and let my trainer sense the revulsion that I felt.

The team from Moorfields Eye hospital arrived to harvest the corneas; the Papworth team from Cambridge came to take her heart and lungs. Yes, perversely, "harvest" is the term we surgeons use for donor organ retrieval – a word that in a child's schoolbook conjures up sights and smells of bounty, health and life.

True that in many ways, Amelia would live on. She would live as a gift of life to several grateful fellow human beings now restored to health and vitality.

She would also live on… in the memory of a complete stranger.

*

I forced myself to look away from Amelia. My attention came back to Meenakshi, as she walked by my side on our way home. She had the buoyant stride of a happy, vibrant teenager. I leaned my head as my daughter talked.

'You know, Jacqui's promised to take me on the woodland tracks as soon as I'm confident on the saddle. And Dad, you can buy me all my livery stuff in Woldingham Saddlery. Becks says they've got an amazing range.'

'And riding hats Munni? I asked.

'Of course Dad.'

She chatted on as we walked.

I listened, I even smiled; I did not interrupt for a single moment.

I stifled my fears.

CHAPTER 6

Haematuria (blood in the urine) – some technical aspects

This short chapter is an attempt to de-mystify the most important keyhole operation for bladder cancer. Investing a few precious minutes would also give a better understanding of what happened to Marjorie in the next story.

Medical acronyms used in this chapter:

USC – urgent suspected cancer
CT – computerised tomography
MDT – multi-disciplinary team
MDM – multi-disciplinary meeting
TURBT – trans-urethral resection of bladder tumour

*

The sight of blood in the urine is alarming. It is a fearful discovery in the loneliness of a bleak privy, like a breast lump in the shower.

Under ordinary circumstances, most of us are not squeamish about seeing blood. Everyone's had a nose-bleed sometime or other. We nick ourselves shaving, and accidental minor cuts and scrapes do not cause undue worry.

It is the unexpected sight of blood that's frightening.

Haematuria or blood in the urine is one such situation, as is also blood in the stools. Both necessitate *urgent* consultation with our GP.

This is because blood in the urine may be due to cancer of the kidney or bladder. In cases of blood in the stools, bowel cancer is a sinister possibility and must be promptly investigated.

In Britain, men and women with haematuria are seen by a cancer specialist within two weeks of the general practitioner sending a faxed referral to the local district general hospital. This expedited hospital booking is known as a USC (Urgent Suspected Cancer) referral. It is an NHS target introduced by the UK government to speed up diagnosis, so that cancer specialists are able to catch the disease early, and as a consequence treat early, thereby improving outcome.

A white envelope franked with the hospital's stamp drops in the letter box within a day, perhaps two, of the GP's referral to the hospital's cancer office. The letter inside gives an appointment date and provides details of tests at a specially organised haematuria clinic.

The tests include an ultrasound scan and a camera examination of the bladder under local anaesthetic. A CT scan is also arranged in most instances.

The camera examination, or "look inside" the bladder, is performed by inserting through the urethra a delicate fibre-optic tube known as a flexible cystoscope. This instrument is slim, much like the flex of a hair dryer and is equally supple. As such it negotiates the natural bends of the urethra easily. Liberal use of local anaesthetic jelly reduces discomfort to a minimum. The luminous fibre-optic system of the flexible cystoscope shows up the inside of the bladder with pin sharp images that would match the latest HD colour television.

After completion of tests at the haematuria clinic, many of us would be reassured and sent back to our GP for treatment of minor ailments such as urinary infections. For others, relief would come in the shape of non-life-threatening findings, such as a kidney or bladder stone or simply a big prostate, all of which can be dealt with by a urologist.

For some of us however, a diagnosis of kidney or bladder cancer would be life-changing.

*

With kidney cancer, a special 3-phase CT scan shows how far the tumour has grown, whether it has invaded nearby organs and blood vessels, or shot off satellite clumps of cancer cells known as metastases to the lungs, bones and liver.

Thereafter, the scans are reviewed by the urology multi-disciplinary team (MDT), comprising surgeons, oncologists, specialist nurses, radiologists and pathologists.

Our MDT in Croydon meets at noon every Thursday in the hospital's postgraduate medical centre for an hour and a half, often longer. All the kidney, bladder, prostate and testis cancer cases of the week are discussed at this multi-disciplinary meeting (MDM) and consensus decisions taken on the most appropriate form of treatment for each patient.

In the NHS, most people with kidney cancer undergo curative surgery (radical nephrectomy whereby the cancerous kidney along with its fatty envelope and lymph nodes are excised) within a few weeks of diagnosis.

In cases of bladder cancer, an operation would be booked with the same urgency.

This operation is known as TURBT, trans-urethral resection of bladder tumour and is carried out under general or spinal anaesthesia.

To perform TURBT, the urological surgeon uses a different cystoscope – a metallic instrument, which is rigid and wider than the slender flexible cystoscope. It is about the thickness of a fountain pen. The larger bore is necessary, as the lumen of this operating cystoscope needs to be roomy enough for the surgeon to pass down into the bladder, twin parallel wires of a cutting and coagulating device as extensions of his operating fingers.

Thus equipped, the urological surgeon, like a skilled puppeteer, conducts and controls nimble actions far away from his fingertips. His stage being the inside of the bladder.

With the rigid cystoscope (as with the flexible), the light system provides brilliant illumination and a magnified view of the bladder interior. An integrated video camera arrangement captures the colour images and transfers them to an adjoining television screen, which is positioned at eye level, in front of the surgeon.

The anaesthetised patient lies supine on the operating table in the lithotomy position, in which the patient rests on his back with the legs lifted up and parted, to provide access to the genitalia and perineum (the area between the scrotum/vagina and the anus). The legs are supported on stirrups with the hips and knees flexed.

This lithotomy position is so named as historically it provided the lithotomist (a bygone practitioner skilled in the art of lithotomy or bladder stone removal) the easiest access to make his cut through the perineal skin straight into the urethra and then to insert either his finger or instruments inside the bladder to winkle out the stone.

In those earlier days, lithotomy was performed without anaesthesia. Lightning speed was used instead! William Cheselden, an early eighteenth-century surgeon at St Thomas' Hospital, made his reputation, and his fortune, by achieving the feat of carrying out lithotomy stone extraction with his patient squirming for less than a minute. Why did men put up with this dreaded operation? It's because the pain, as anyone who's ever had a bladder or kidney stone knows, is limitless. The Belgian king, Leopold the First, could only sleep standing up – the one position in which the stone rolled away from the most sensitive part of his bladder!

Nowadays, with his patient in the lithotomy position, the surgeon sits on a wheelie chair, with his working area right in front. He has a clear unhindered view of the operation he's performing inside the urinary bladder, on the conveniently positioned TV monitor.

Moreover, everyone present in the operating theatre is able to see the keyhole surgery in real time, which has the advantage of inculcating a greater sense of participation. This includes the awake patient who's been given a spinal anaesthetic.

Many of my patients have been fascinated watching

their operation in progress. 'I could see *everything* Mr Das. When you turned that laser on, it was like a blowtorch blasting away the tumour.'

During TURBT, we use sterile saline solution to fill up and expand the bladder in order to improve vision while operating. The saline solution goes in through a side channel of the cystoscope which has been connected by tubing to an overhanging fluid bag.

Usually, the tumour appears as a fronded fleshy growth - the imaginative textbook description is that of a sea anemone, with the fronds of the tumour swaying in the saline flow, resembling the undulating tentacles of the ocean creature.

We are able to cut away the tumour using a fine copper wire loop, shaped as a half-moon, down which an electric current is passed. The loop is attached to the ends of the parallel wires mentioned earlier that are inserted through the working channel of the cystoscope. In recent times, we sometimes use a laser beam to do the cutting. Through the same working channel, we can then retrieve the cut away or resected chips of tumour by using a clever mini-vacuum device that "hoovers" out the tumour chips from inside the bladder.

The collected specimen chips are then dropped in a pot containing preservative solution, and sent away to the laboratory for microscopic analysis by the pathologist.

At the end of the TURBT operation, a catheter is slipped into the bladder. The patient is then transferred to the recovery room. Here, a syringeful of an indigo blue liquid is slowly pushed into the bladder through the catheter. This fluid contains a potent chemotherapy drug, which kills off any microscopic clumps of cancer cells that may have escaped.

Most men and women with bladder cancer are effectively treated by this combination of keyhole surgery and local chemotherapy.

A small number of people, less than ten per cent of all bladder cancer cases, have highly aggressive tumours. Here, a more hard-hitting approach is essential to beat the cancer. This select group is best treated by either major surgery to remove the entire bladder (cystectomy) or radiotherapy. We sometimes need a combination of both. These complex operations and radiotherapy are always carried out in special tertiary hospitals designated as cancer centres like the Royal Marsden and St George's Hospital.

CHAPTER 7

Marjorie

Croydon – 2001

Marjorie Treacher was a genial sixty-seven-year-old, fit and active grandmother who'd lived in Croydon all her life. She and her husband Frank were churchwardens in their Sanderstead parish.

Marjorie had a plum-sized bladder tumour.

'It's like a wart inside your bladder, Mrs Treacher,' said the associate specialist who'd carried out Marjorie's cystoscopy, describing to her the growth that had caused the bleeding in her urine.

Marjorie's next hospital appointment was at the uro-oncology clinic with Maureen, our clinical nurse specialist and myself. We were going to discuss with her, the operative treatment that she needed. She came to meet us, accompanied by a young woman in her early twenties.

'This is my granddaughter Carla. She's the clever one in the family. Carla's doing a degree at Croydon College.'

Marjorie was not at all fazed when told that she had to come in for an operation.

'I'd my gall bladder taken out last year. The womb operation Mr Grant did was before that… and, all four of my children were born here.'

'So you know our hospital well, Mrs Treacher,' I said.

'Very well. I also do voluntary work for the Friends,' she replied, referring to our hospital charity, the Friends of Mayday.

Maureen and I then explained the TURBT procedure.

'So this is all going to be keyhole surgery, Mr Das?' Carla asked.

'Yes, all done through a telescope, no cuts on your grandma's tummy,' Maureen said.

Marjorie's face crinkled when Carla turned to her with an impish smile.

'Well Grandma, this time you won't have a big scar to show off!'

*

Marjorie was first on our morning list that Thursday. We knew from the preliminary cystoscopy in the haematuria clinic and the CT scan, that this was a large tumour that had grown in a thickened bladder wall. This information suggested the probability of a rapidly growing invasive cancer.

James, our experienced specialist registrar scrubbed up to do the operation. He'd done many before during his training.

I was happy for James to do the operation without myself peering over his shoulder. James had completed his training and had passed the exit exam, the FRCS Urol. His Certificate of Completion of Training had come through a few months ago. James was biding his time for a suitable consultant job to come up.

Earlier that morning, I had been called to see if I could

come for an urgent meeting with our surgical division manager in his office.

I had said yes, as I'd be near at hand within the hospital while James did the TURBT.

The urgent meeting called by the manager was to deal with "breaches". We had failed to see two out of forty-six USC referrals for the last quarter within the stipulated two weeks, and had therefore breached our target.

Although a small percentage for that period, this was such an important cancer target that we'd immediately come up on the radar.

Such breaches of cancer targets attract punitive fines for the hospital trust. The chief executive gets shirty emails. He, in turn, frowns down the line.

As the senior surgeon in the department and the urology cancer lead, the buck stopped with me.

At the meeting, we began by looking into the root cause of the breaches. In one instance, the patient had moved home and had not received her appointment letter.

Whilst we were looking into the other, my pager buzzed. The display flashed the urology theatre extension with a terse message asking me to call urgently.

Angela, our senior theatre sister answered at the first ring.

'James is struggling a bit. The bleeding's making his view on the TV monitor hazy.'

'Does he want me to come up?' I asked.

There was a pause during which I could hear a muffled conversation.

'He says he's going to stop resecting and do some coagulation to control the bleeding.'

'OK, let me know how he gets on, ring me on this extension.'

But I couldn't settle and just carry on with the meeting. I had worked with Angela for over fifteen years and had great respect for her gut instincts. She was an experienced theatre sister. Angela wouldn't call me unless she was concerned. I decided not to wait.

As I got up to leave the meeting, with the business manager in mid-sentence, the phone rang. It was James himself. In a voice that I'd not heard before from this confident young man, he said, 'I really need some help here. Can you come right away?'

*

I pushed open the swing doors of Theatre 2. I was already in my scrubs having gone to the breach meeting wearing a spare white coat over my theatre blues.

It was evident that there was a perforation of the bladder. The view on the television monitor was a "red out" with no identifiable structures or landmarks. The abdomen looked distended although the saline inflow had been stopped. I placed the palm of my hand on the tummy under the sterile drapes. It was cardboard rigid, distended with all the fluid that had escaped from the hole in the bladder into the peritoneal cavity.

I knew immediately that we had to open up the abdomen and over-sew the perforation in the bladder wall.

I started to scrub while Marjorie's legs were being taken down from the lithotomy position to straighten her flat on the operating table.

Angela had already anticipated the laparotomy (opening the abdomen), and had brought out the requisite instrument set.

Our super-efficient, cool and collected, consultant anaesthetist, Dr Murali, did not need to have things spelled out. He too had made his preparations for the change from keyhole surgery to a longer, bigger open operation.

After prepping the skin with orange-brown povidone-iodine antiseptic, we swiftly opened the abdomen with a scalpel blade, incising along the midline from belly-button to just above the pubic bone.

About a litre of blood-stained fluid gushed out from the peritoneal cavity, and was rapidly sucked away.

We packed away loops of bowel from the pelvis, using wet extra-large swabs. We could now see a big tear near the dome of the bladder. We also saw that the inner cavity was full of tumour with hardly any part of the bladder wall uninvolved by cancer.

It was evident that there was little salvageable bladder left. Trying to cobble up the perforation by suturing would not work. The sutures would cut out, we wouldn't be able to control the bleeding, *and* we'd be leaving cancerous tissue behind.

There was little option other than to carry out a cystectomy, removing the entire bladder.

I looked up at my anaesthetist.

'Murali, sorry, we'll have to do a cystectomy here.'

It was like a pilot telling his navigator that the route had abruptly changed. Instead of cruising from Heathrow to Manchester, they'd be flying onto Newfoundland, and rather than landing on an airport runway, they were going to put down on a field at the foot of a mountain.

Cystectomy involves excising the entire bladder and urethra, along with the pelvic lymph nodes.

Thereafter, we would fashion a new urine drainage system, a urinary conduit – first isolating a segment of ileum, the terminal part of the small intestine. This ileal loop would have two ends. The ureters, the tubes that connect the kidneys to the bladder, would be stitched to the end of the ileal loop that remained inside the abdomen.

The other end would be brought outside to the surface through a small hole in the right lower quadrant of the abdomen as a stoma, through which urine would trickle out and be collected in a stoma bag.

*

We hadn't consented Marjorie for this herculean four-hour operation involving a large cut in her belly, intestinal surgery and a permanent stoma. All that she was expecting was a catheter for one, perhaps two days, after her TURBT.

Nonetheless, we had no other choice in this challenging situation.

Once the decision was taken, we proceeded swiftly with the cystectomy. It wasn't too difficult to remove what was left of the bladder. There was some scarring at the back of the pelvis from the previous hysterectomy, but overall we didn't struggle, and there was no further major blood loss. The rest of the operation to form the ileal loop and stoma also went smoothly. By the time we put in the skin clips, the theatre clock showed that it had taken us just under three hours to finish.

The scrub nurse smoothed a stoma bag over the pink healthy urostomy. The first drops of crystal clear urine sparkled through the transparent stoma bag. We helped transfer Marjorie from the operating table to her trolley, and wheeled her to the recovery suite.

*

Marjorie was told about the entire drama the next morning once she was back in Bensham 2 ward. She listened carefully as I sat beside her on the bed, with the ward sister and James standing by. She didn't arch her eyebrows while I explained the reason why a thirty–forty-minute keyhole procedure had to be converted to a surgical marathon.

She was not disconcerted by her unexpected tummy incision and she was fascinated with her stoma.

Over the next few days, she impressed her stoma therapist by quickly becoming adept at changing her stoma bags.

She scored 10/10 with the ward nurses by rapidly getting back on her feet. She stayed in bed as little as possible, walking around the ward, chatting with the other patients – a familiar figure in her maroon patterned dressing gown. She adjusted to not sitting on a toilet seat to empty her bladder, making the jocose observation 'Don't have to get up at night to go to the loo now.'

*

I next met Marjorie at her second follow-up outpatient appointment eight weeks after she'd been discharged home. Her granddaughter Carla was with her this time as well. I was delighted that everything was going well for Marjorie. She had gone back to her busy life.

When I asked how she was getting on with the stoma, her smile widened and her blue-grey eyes lit up with an impish sparkle.

'Mr Das, I've told all my friends about you, and how good you've all been to me.'

Maureen and I listened with attention.

'I said to them - "I came for just a camera job and my consultant ended up doing this really big operation. Afterwards, he was so pleased with me that he even presented me with a special handbag which I carry with me all the time even when I go to sleep"!'

As they left the clinic room, Carla said to me while shaking hands, 'Mr Das, she hasn't told you, but every night, Grandma says a little prayer for you.'

CHAPTER 8

The Big "C"
Ramesh's story

Croydon – 2010

Like every other morning of the week, Ramesh Mehta was getting ready for work. An affable, somewhat portly gentleman in his mid-fifties, he ran his own accounting firm from an office in West Croydon, specialising in helping small businesses. His first appointment that Tuesday was with an old client, the owner of the local car repair workshop in Thornton Heath, the bustling heart of the borough.

*

Ramesh smoked his first cigarette of the day with his breakfast cup of strong Assam tea. He had cut down the sugar in his tea and coffee to just one small spoon, encouraged by his GP, given the family history of type 2 diabetes and ischaemic heart disease. Recently, Ramesh had also joined a local gym. It was however, proving more of a struggle to give up smoking altogether.

He ground out his cigarette and drained his teacup before going to the toilet. Thankfully, Ramesh had no problems in that department. Unlike many of his fifty-plus-something friends at the Asian men's Dosti Club in Norbury, he didn't get up at night to pee, and he still had a strong "competitive" urinary stream.

It was an utter shock when he noticed the bright red in the arc of his urine flow. At first, there was the momentary denial, rapidly followed by alarm, as he witnessed the irrefutable confirmation noisily colouring the toilet pan.

Ramesh didn't say anything to his wife Asha, whose gaze was fixed on the screen of her laptop placed beside a coffee mug on the kitchen table – she had a deadline to meet for the graphic design contract from the Council.

Ramesh got through his early morning meeting with Lloyd Carter, the Lewisham-born Jamaican car workshop owner, quietly suppressing the apprehension that sat at the back of his mind like an immovable deadweight. As soon as he'd ushered out his client, he revisited the toilet. There was no relief from anxiety. He passed more blood in the urine, this time with a few small clots.

He returned to his office, locked the door and googled "blood in urine". The NHS website, though sensitively worded, did not allay his worries. Terms such as "tumour" and "growth" conjured up disquieting possibilities that further unsettled him. Sensibly, the website information included advice to seek an expeditious appointment with the GP.

The practice nurse to whom Ramesh was put through when he rang his South Croydon GP surgery was able to arrange an urgent consultation with one of the doctors the very next day.

*

Dr Michael Johnson took a succinct history and asked Ramesh to lie on the couch. The doctor felt around Ramesh's abdomen and genitals. He then gently inserted a gloved finger in the rectum to check the prostate.

'Can't find anything wrong on the examination, Mr Mehta,' the GP said, washing his hands.

Dr Johnson added, 'We need to do some more tests for which I'll refer you to the hospital. They'll do a scan of your kidneys and a camera examination of your bladder. The tests won't take long, and don't worry, the camera inspection doesn't hurt as they use lots of local anaesthetic jelly.'

With an innate, as well as professional consideration, the GP also said, 'It'll all be done on the same day, and they'll tell you the results at the end.'

The GP faxed a referral to the cancer office of our hospital requesting an urgent appointment.

*

The fear of cancer, the big "C", as many of us describe it with a mixture of dread and awe, once raised, can assume monstrous proportions in our minds. Ramesh was no exception. It seemed that there was so much of it around – discussions on radio and television, newspaper headlines on cancer survival in the UK compared to the European Union, friends and relatives unexpectedly diagnosed with breast, bowel and prostate cancer. There was a half-page article in that week's *Croydon Argus* on the prevalence of kidney cancer in Asian men, which seemed to point straight at him.

In his mind, fear kept widening its rings like a pebble flung into a lake. Fear was the one thing that took over Ramesh's life while he waited to be seen at the hospital.

The appointment came through in less than two weeks. He was asked to attend a clinic specially designated to investigate cases of haematuria (blood in the urine).

On the morning of his hospital appointment, Ramesh was welcomed and checked in by the desk clerk at the haematuria clinic. A few minutes after he'd sat down, a staff nurse handed Ramesh a sterile pot with instructions to provide a mid-stream sample of urine. Two 10 ml vials of blood were taken from his arm.

Soon after this, he was taken to the endoscopy suite where one of our experienced associate specialists inspected the inside of his bladder with a special flexible telescope copiously lubricated with local anaesthetic jelly. Ramesh hardly felt any discomfort. He was distracted and totally absorbed by the moving picture being revealed in sharp detail on the television screen digitally connected to the flexible telescope. His eyes were magnetised by the unfolding contours of the pink inner membranes of his bladder and urethra.

He then had a bit of a wait before being directed to radiology for the ultrasound scan. The young Ethiopian woman sonographer, in a smart white uniform, gave Ramesh a bright smile and asked him to take off his shirt before lying down on the couch. She smeared coupling gel on his flanks and proceeded to run the ultrasound probe smoothly with gentle pressure.

Without moving her gaze from the flickering shadows on the luminous screen of the scanner machine, she whispered breathlessly, 'Left kidney good,' talking half to herself.

Moving over to the right, she struck up a conversation with her patient.

'Where you live, Mr Mehta?'

'In Norbury, two bus stops from the hospital.'

Ramesh waited for a response. Minutes passed. The young radiographer's confident manner seemed to falter. She kept moving the probe without being able to hone in on the correct spot. Her breath whistled as an audible rasp in the small room. Soon, a silence enveloped the two figures joined by a sonic transducer, a hush that turned sinister. She dug the conical tip of the probe deeper under the ribs, making Ramesh wince, the pressure being applied as though to coax the right kidney into an answer.

'Something there, not sure,' she finally said, her English now heavily layered with the Amharic of her native land.

Several 'tsk, tsk's followed as she kept trying to focus on a particular area, heightening Ramesh's rising alarm.

After what seemed an eternity, she gave up with an, 'I go check with consultant.'

The sonographer returned some ten minutes later… the consultant radiologist was tied up with a liver biopsy and couldn't come to the scanning room. He had recommended a CT scan, to determine the uncertain shadow in the right kidney, which the sonographer had tried but failed to pin down.

By now, convinced that he had kidney cancer, Ramesh went to the CT office. He was told that the earliest appointment would not be for another six days.

He came home feeling physically all right, just a little

tired. It was his mind that had to bear the brunt of coping with the intruder. His day at the hospital, rather than allaying anxiety, had heightened the lacerating knot of fear. If only he could go into hibernation, a deep sleep till the day of his CT scan, when he would know, one way or the other. But life doesn't work like that, for, just as the cliché says – life goes on, work has to be done, conversations tolerated, meals eaten, taxes paid...

This was also the time of *Navratri* (literally nine nights), the biggest festival in the calendar for the Gujarati community. For those nine nights and days, the goddess Durga, in her avatar as Shakti or Supreme Power, would be worshipped.

Prayers would be offered throughout the day. In the evening, as throngs of extended families of grandparents, mums and dads, aunts and uncles, and excited children joined in, celebrations of song and dance would commence and continue late into the night.

The festivities for the Croydon and Tooting Gujarati fraternity were being held in Wandsworth Town Hall, large enough to accommodate the dense mass of families, turned out in their celebratory best. Equally important were the two generous car parks, ensuring plentiful capacity for the fleets of Jaguars, Audis and Mercedes of this thrifty British Indian mercantile community, whose business acumen, beginning with a unique ability to operate successful family-run, mid-size enterprises, had won paeans from successive Chancellors of the Exchequer.

Ramesh wore a smart charcoal safari suit as he accompanied Asha, resplendent in peacock blue silk sari with worked silver border. At the entrance, they were greeted by Jignesh, a young pharmacist with his own high street outlet, and organising secretary of the *Navratri* celebrations committee.

'Hello Uncle, hello Asha Auntie, you both look great... just like a Bollywood couple.'

'Thanks Jignesh. How's your dad?'

'He's at home now; the hospital discharged him last week. Please go through, the *Garba* is about to start.'

Ramesh and Asha entered the big hall and took ringside seats.

Soon the Grand Chamber was a mesmerising mass of colour, sound and motion – the traditional dance, the *Ras Garba*, had begun.

Two concentric circles of dancers, one clockwise, the other counter-clockwise, moved in a slow choreographed rhythm to the percussive beats of the drum-like *dhols*.

The men were in traditional costumes of heaped turban, short rounded *kurtas* and hugging pajamas.

The women wore colourful, embroidered *cholis* (midriff-baring blouses fastened at the back), and flared skirt-like *lehengas*. The *cholis* were patterned with sequins, beads, shells, and tiny mirrors. The women performers were also adorned with a surfeit of gold ornaments – many-tiered necklaces of intricate design; large drooping *jhumka* earrings; rows of heavy clattering bracelets.

All the dancers held *dandiyas* – light, decorated bamboo sticks. Every so often, in sequential regularity, the moving circles would pause – opposing pairs of dancers would face each other, and lightly strike their *dandiyas* with a gentle crack.

The graceful swirl of the many-coloured, long skirts

of supple female forms, the kaleidoscope effect created by shards of light bouncing off the tiny mirrors stitched into the women's blouses, the soft '*thuk*' as the dandiya sticks struck, temporarily distracted Ramesh.

At one point, the plump man in the next seat, noisily munching crisps, turned to him. After a brief scrutiny, the man extended his hand and said, 'Ramesh Mehta, hanh? Haven't seen you in years.'

He looked more closely, tilting back his head to better use his bifocals, 'You've not aged at all.'

The man then leaned forward, looked past Ramesh, and said with a playful smile, 'Mrs Mehta must be taking very good care of you.'

*

Later in the evening, back at home, away from the sound, light and music, the melancholy of fear, which was waiting like a furtive cat burglar, struck with pent-up vindictiveness.

Wisely, Ramesh resisted the temptation of unstoppering the decanter, two-thirds filled with Johnnie Walker Black Label. He persuaded himself to step into the prayer room, unrolled the vinyl yoga mat, sat cross-legged and closed his eyes. The meditation helped him wrest five hours of sleep, from which he woke well before the alarm clock.

The next five days followed the same pattern of work and enforced festivity, with only variations of detail.

*

His wife, Asha, was with him for the CT scan. She'd gone the evening before to the Oshwal temple near London Road with an offering of fruit and petals. After prayers, the surprisingly young Hindu priest, with a marked Estuary accent that seemed incongruous with the *tilak* of sandalwood paste on his forehead, assured Asha of a propitious outcome. She convinced herself that this must be so, though a kernel of doubt remained stubbornly lodged in her mind.

The CT scan was much quicker than they'd anticipated. The receptionist in the CT office, Gayatri, had known Asha and Ramesh for many years at the Gujarati community centre in South Croydon. She asked them to wait while she went into the consultant's cubbyhole with a personal request.

A few minutes later, Dr Tony Newman-Sanders, tall good-looking consultant radiologist, with shirt sleeves rolled up, forelock askew, tie tucked inside his shirt, came out to reception where Ramesh and Asha were sitting in adjoining chairs pulled close. Dr Newman-Sander's advancing smile matched his broad, outstretched hand.

'You don't have cancer, Mr Mehta. It's only a kidney stone.' He curled his forefinger near the tip of his thumb. 'The size of a mulberry.'

*

A few weeks later, we pulverised the stone with shock waves using a million-dollar, German-engineered machine. Ramesh lay back comfortably on a couch while 20 inches from his flank, the machine's generator beamed

85

the shock waves. At the end of the forty-five-minute treatment session, there was not even a scratch on his skin. For the next few days, Ramesh passed tiny bits of grit in his urine. X-rays, taken the following week, looked as though he never had a kidney stone.

CHAPTER 9

The Healing Touch

Croydon – 2006

The Monday morning urology clinic was running late. Urgent cases had been added on to an already onerous list.

I hurried over to outpatients at the end of the morning ward round. There'd been an influx of emergency admissions over the weekend, and by the time we had seen the last inpatient in Bensham 2, it was nearly quarter past nine.

I nodded to the waiting staff nurse and pushed open the door to my clinic room in main outpatients, trying to appear unruffled despite being late.

Inside the clinic room, I switched on the lights and opened the swing windows to let in some fresh air. I briskly draped my suit jacket on the back of the swivel chair and dropped my briefcase on the pastel L-shaped table.

The press of a button woke the computer screen. Swaying images appeared, settled into the funky multi-colour hospital logo, and demanded my username and password.

After a stolen glance at my wristwatch, I picked up the top set of notes from the nearest of three heaped piles, pushed back the swivel chair and went out to call the first patient.

The common waiting area, the size of a large gymnasium, was already filling with patients who had appointments for urology, vascular surgery, and neurology clinics.

Soon they would chafe at the delay in being seen. Several would have to go back to the public car parks to top up rapacious meters.

The appointment clerks kept their gaze down and voices low as they dealt with the person in front, trying to ignore the lengthening, fidgety queue behind.

I'd just seen the third patient, an aggressive teenager with a glinting lower lip piercing, whose bladder and mind had been wrecked by ketamine drug abuse, when the phone rang. It was Christine from surgical admissions.

'How're you this lovely Monday morning?'

'Running late and the registrar's still stuck in theatre with an emergency.'

'Your laser prostatectomy for Thursday's been cancelled by pre-op. They found an arrhythmia on ECG and want him sorted out by cardiology.'

'Hmm, OK, can we get in the urgent bladder tumour to fill the slot?'

'Hah! Thought you'd say that... I've already spoken to Mr Rabjohn's wife, who's much happier now.'

Other interruptions peppered the morning – the business manager asking if she could pop in for a minute to discuss the waiting list, the postgraduate centre administrator to remind me of next week's talk to GPs on men's health and prostate cancer...

Midway through the clinic, I got up to call in the next

patient, a male new referral. I opened the clinic door, and was again pierced by the searchlight of a hundred stares. I avoided looking directly at any of those searing eyes, fastened my gaze at a point in the middle of the mass, between adjacent shoulders, and called out, 'Mr Tarzi, Mr Karim Tarzi please.'

In my peripheral vision, I saw a youngish man in his mid-thirties rise quickly from the edge of the crowd. I went back into my clinic room, not daring to catch any reproachful disappointed eye. In a further act of pusillanimity, I held the door open from inside.

The mid-thirties man dressed in suit and tie hurried in; behind him was a tall elderly gentleman with a neatly trimmed white beard. He was wearing a thick woollen sweater inside his jacket although it was June.

The young man took the chair nearest to me at the L-table.

'I've come with my father. He doesn't speak much English.'

The revelation produced a mild look of embarrassment in the older man who seemed to understand what'd been said. His smile nevertheless, did not constrict.

'No worries, I see from the GP's letter that your father's been having urinary problems.'

'Yes, he gets up often at night and he isn't that good during the day.'

'How long's this been going on?'

'We've noticed ever since he came to live with us from Pakistan, and that's about six months.'

I turned to the gentleman in his late sixties who had been sitting quietly next to his son.

I asked softly, '*Aap ka pishaab ke taqleef hain?*' (Do you have trouble passing urine?)

'*Ji, kaafi taqleef,*' he replied. (Yes, a lot of trouble.)

There was no awkwardness in the exchange – it was as though a conversation between a British consultant surgeon and his patient in an NHS hospital using a language of distant shores was as natural as English breakfast tea.

Though nowhere near fluent, I could hold a reasonable conversation in Urdu which always delighted my Pakistani patients and, for that moment at least, erased the troublesome border with my native India.

The older man's suited and booted son looked somewhat discomfited, even annoyed. His expression suggested that had he known the consultant could speak Urdu, he wouldn't have bothered to take the morning off from the office. Dammit, couldn't the outpatient appointment office have told him this before?

I learned from sixty-nine-year old Mr Karim Tarzi that even in Pakistan, he'd been suffering with his waterworks.

What distressed him most was leakage of urine. There was the frustrating dribble at the end of peeing when he thought that he'd finished and done up his trousers.

In addition, there was also that hot little spurt which came without any warning whatsoever. Those few recalcitrant drops soiled his pants and left him unclean.

This was all the more of a problem as he could never be fully clean before *namaaz* prayers and when he wanted to go to the mosque.

In Islam, the faithful perform the ritual of *Wudu*, the special ablution of washing face, hands and feet before reciting the *Shahada*, which is the affirmation of faith. The cleansed devotee declares 'There is no god but God and Muhammed is His messenger'. Soiled trousers deprive the devout of the purity essential before submission to God.

'Doctor sahib, my body is never clean. I feel ashamed. How can I stand before Allah if I'm impure?'

To put him at ease, I shifted the focus of conversation, and asked, 'Where in Pakistan did you live, sir?'

It turned out that he was an Achakzai Pashtun. His family originally hailed from the rocky Spin Boldak division of Afghanistan's Kandahar district. I could see in my mind's eye William Dalrymple's picturesque description of blue-eyed children agile as the mountain goats, and fierce tribesmen battling both the British and Russian empires, aiming their matchlocks with the eye of a hawk, swooping down the scree brandishing raised swords. The Pashtuns had jealously guarded their independent way of life. Practice of the Sunni Islam faith was an important aspect of who they were.

'Doctor sahib, where are *you* from?' he asked.

'I was born in India, Calcutta,' I replied.

'Aah, Indiaah! My grandfather came to India when he was a young man.' Happy memories of childhood tales shone in Mr Tarzi's eyes. He added, 'There was no separate Pakistan in those days.'

I learned that the family settled in Lahore at a time when Rudyard Kipling was writing his celebrated novel *Kim*, centred on the Lahore of British India. The Tarzis had started a dried fruit business, which thrived. In time, this present Mr Tarzi was able to send his only son Imran to Britain for higher studies.

The son stayed on in England, settling in Croydon where he worked as an accounts officer at the Nestlé headquarters in East Croydon.

'I brought my father over when my mother passed away. My sisters are all married. There was no one in the house with him back home in Lahore.'

'I like it here. So many people from India-Pakistan in Croydon, they all speak my language when I go to shops,' his father joined in.

'He likes the mosque best. Croydon mosque's just walking distance from our house. He's made so many friends there.'

I took Mr Tarzi to the examination couch and asked him to lie on his left side with his knees drawn up. With a gloved index finger inserted in the rectum, I checked his prostate – there was a suspicious nodule.

After he had pulled up his trousers and I'd washed my hands, we went back to sit at the consulting table.

I explained to him in Urdu, 'I found a hard lump in your prostate gland. I'm worried about it. We have to make sure it's not cancer. We need to—'

His son, who had been listening intently, jumped in, 'But my father's never—'

Karim Tarzi raised a hand, his features composed. 'Please continue, Doctor sahib.'

I explained that a biopsy was essential and that it would be carried out within the next seven to ten days.

Imran had a number of questions regarding the biopsy – how it was done, were there any possible complications. He asked, 'Would my father need much looking after at home?'

'It's done with a slim biopsy device attached to an ultrasound probe which is inserted into the rectum, just the way I did the earlier examination,' I said to Imran. 'The biopsy takes about twenty minutes. There's some bleeding in the urine and semen for a few days, and there's a small chance of infection despite the antibiotics we give.'

I ignored the bleep on the computer, alerting me to a new "high importance" email.

'Your father will be able to go home the same day. Make sure you ring the hospital if he has a fever or feels unwell.'

'OK, when do we get the results?'

'In about a week after the biopsy.'

When I turned back to Mr Tarzi, he smiled and clasped my hand. 'It has to be done. It's God's will. I'm happy to be in your care.'

Two weeks later, the biopsy report came to the urology office, part of a sheaf in a fat brown envelope.

On a single white A4 sheet, the Arial black typescript stated, with unfeeling matter-of-fact, what the pathologist had seen under the microscope. The one-line conclusion read – '*poorly-differentiated carcinoma of prostate*'. In plain English, this meant an aggressive prostate cancer.

The appointment to inform Mr Tarzi of the biopsy result took place the following Thursday, at our afternoon uro-oncology clinic. I had beside me our capable and experienced urology nurse specialist, Maureen, who in her early fifties was only just beginning to grey and remained ever cheerful despite an exhaustive workload.

Mr Tarzi was accompanied this time by his daughter-in-law Farzana, a diminutive, round-faced young woman wearing a mauve jumper over *salwar kameez.*

The word "cancer" did not seem to alarm either Mr Tarzi or his daughter-in-law, who spoke with a Lancashire accent.

Maureen and I talked to them about treatment and the need to do an MRI and radio-isotope bone scan to make sure that the cancer hadn't spread.

'Can you do the operation quickly after the scans, Mr Das?' was Farzana's most pressing query.

I reassured her that cancer operations were always high priority. There would be no delay.

Maureen asked Farzana, 'What about your father-in-law, does he have anything to ask Mr Das or myself?'

Intuitively understanding the question, Karim Tarzi raised both palms in the air and gently shook his head.

At the end, he nodded to Maureen and again clasped my hands.

*

His scans confirmed that the prostate cancer had not spread; the urology MDM agreed that he was suitable for an operation to have the cancer removed with a good chance of cure.

The operation is known as radical prostatectomy, where the prostate gland is removed in its entirety along with the pelvic lymph nodes. It is performed only by specialist cancer surgeons with rigorous training and consistently good results, and is exclusively performed in super-specialty hospitals designated as cancer centres – St

George's Hospital in Tooting being our cancer centre for South West Thames.

No operation, however, is without risk and potential complications.

For radical prostatectomy, these include incontinence of urine and impotence.

Incontinence is a hazard because the sphincter muscle that wraps around the urethra, to keep us dry, lies close to the apex of the prostate and can be damaged during surgery.

Usually, there's some mild incontinence after radical prostatectomy which is temporary and resolves after a few weeks, especially if the patient is diligent about post-surgery pelvic floor exercises, and the cancer surgeon has been careful in protecting the sphincter during surgery.

Impotence can occur as the nerves for erection pass down to the penis very close to the prostate, and may be injured during radical prostatectomy. Here too, the surgeon takes every precaution to preserve these erectile nerves.

*

I carried out Karim Tarzi's radical prostatectomy at St George's on my Tuesday morning operating list. The operation went well with minimal blood loss. I felt confident that continence would not be an issue, and that the nerves for erection had been spared. After a few days in Vernon ward, on the fourth floor of St James's Wing, he went home fit and well.

Three weeks after discharge, he came with Farzana to

Croydon for his first post-operative appointment and was seen by Maureen.

After asking about his general health and having ensured that the wound in the lower abdomen was healing well, Maureen said with a smile, 'Now Mr Tarzi, I've got fantastic news this morning. According to the path report, the cancer was totally removed. Mr Das did a good job and took it all away for you. We think there's a very good chance you've been completely cured.'

This good news elicited a wry smile as though there was a skulking "but" waiting to sour the conversation.

Mr Tarzi turned to Farzana, who said, 'But what about his leaking? He tells us he's wet all the time, Maureen.'

'Farzana, this is just temporary. It'll pass in a few weeks.'

Mr Tarzi continued to look doubtful.

'See, he's using only one continence pad a day. I promise you, in a few weeks, he won't need any – he'll be dry,' Maureen said. 'I'm also going to ask the continence clinic nurses to show him exercises which'll strengthen the pelvic muscles.'

*

A couple of weeks later, I was in my office sifting through the week's referrals when I heard a knock. This was not a diffident tap seeking permission; this was a confident rap announcing presence. I looked up from the pile of paperwork and smiled, for I knew who it was.

My secretary Angi poked in a glossy head.

'Hi, I've just taken a message from Mr Tarzi's son.'

Angi has been with me over ten years. Despite that

long sentence, our resident seraph of the urology office has remained as fresh and gracile as on her first day.

'Imran says his father's still very wet. He's asking if he could see you for a quick word.'

I arranged to meet Imran in Bensham 2 at the end of my evening ward round the same week. He came on his own after work, again in office suit and tie.

His father's main worry was urine leakage. It was nearly a month after the operation.

'You see he can't pray as he's not clean. He's stopped going to the mosque. He's getting withdrawn and more depressed.'

I assured Imran that this was still within the "early days" time-frame. Was his father doing the pelvic floor exercises regularly?

'I believe he is. Dad didn't come today as he doesn't like going out these days. But if you're prepared to speak to him on the phone, it'd be a great help. He has a lot of faith in you Mr Das.'

I called him the next morning. I avoided medical jargon and encouraged him to persevere with the pelvic exercises. I ended with assuring him, '*Inshallah*, in just a few weeks, all will be well.'

There were no further calls from the Tarzis after this conversation.

*

Six weeks later, I saw his name on my list for the Thursday afternoon cancer follow-up clinic.

He came alone, dressed in the flowing robes of his

native North West Frontier Province. Adding to his 6 ft stature was a jaunty dark-navy cap.

'*Salaam alaikum*, Doctor sahib,' he greeted from the door. His smile stayed with us, as he sat down and said 'Hello' to Maureen and the two medical students.

Before I could even ask, he inclined his head and said, '*Hanh, sab bilkul thik hain.*' (Yes, *everything* is perfectly fine.)

He answered the rest of the questions on Maureen's checklist in cheerful affirmation. We arranged to see him again for a routine follow-up appointment in three months.

Before he left, Mr Tarzi reached out and took both my hands, examining them closely as though searching for something precious. After a few moments, he said, 'Doctor sahib, perhaps you are not aware of this – you are blessed by Allah. *Aap ke haath mein shifaah hain.*' (There is *shifaah* in your hands.)

I was not entirely sure what he meant as I was unfamiliar with the word *shifaah*. Nonetheless, it sounded like something good, so I thanked him and wished him well.

After he'd left, I turned to Yasmin, one the medical students. Yasmin was grinning.

'Wow, Mr Das,' she said, pushing up her round blue-framed glasses. 'That's *some* compliment. *Shifaah* is Arabic for healing touch. I think it's even mentioned in the Koran.'

*

That evening, when I got back to Grove House, I found my daughter Meenakshi at home for the weekend from her digs at the LSE. She was in the kitchen, cooking lasagne.

'Would you like some, Dad?'

Gratefully replying to the affirmative, I kicked off my shoes, poured a glass of Rioja and turned on the TV in the adjoining living room. Soon, I was engrossed in *EastEnders*, my own private foible; my unrepentant form of escapism.

I did not hear Meenakshi come in through the connecting archway with my dinner.

She tapped my shoulder and handed me a plate of steaming lasagne, along with a paper napkin and a fork. My gaze remained fixed on Barbara Windsor in the flinty persona of Peggy Mitchell, delivering yet another cheesy denouement on a hapless Frank Butcher.

As I reached out distractedly, the fork slipped through my fingers to clatter on the parquet.

Meenakshi reached down, and before I could apologise, said with the asperity of a long-suffering offspring, 'Honestly Dad, you've *such* clumsy hands!'

CHAPTER 10

"Not to do Nonsense"

The Royal College of Physicians and Surgeons, Glasgow –
1980

'Good luck old chap,' my boss said as he signed my study leave form, granting permission for travel, with expenses, to sit the Primary FRCS exam in Glasgow.

Frank Tasker Wheeldon FRCS, 6 ft 2, ramrod straight, white-maned senior consultant orthopaedic surgeon at Mount Gould Hospital, Plymouth had himself taken the Primary FRCS more than thirty years ago. Yet the memory lingered.

'Some of my chums needed more than a couple of shots at the dashed thing,' he reminisced looking at me, his senior house surgeon, with those penetrating blue-grey eyes, that according to the orthopaedic theatre nurses, completed his resemblance to James Mason.

Clutching the signed piece of paper, I went off to fill up the three-page application form that had come from Glasgow.

*

The Royal College of Physicians and Surgeons of Glasgow was founded in 1599 by Royal Charter, granted by King

James VI to a surgeon, a physician and an apothecary. The College is housed in an impressive porticoed historical building on 242 St Vincent Street.

Apart from Fellows of the College, who'd already gained admission by clearing the hurdle of exacting examinations, the Royal College also witnesses a dense footfall from a subaltern brigade of junior doctors who come to sit the exams.

Attaining a Fellowship of any of the four Royal Colleges, that of England, Edinburgh, Glasgow or Ireland, pushes open heavy doors – the successful trainee may now place a foot on the first rung of a rigorous training ladder in his or her aspiration to climb to the pinnacle – to attain the rank of consultant surgeon.

The examinations are in two parts. Success in both confers the hallowed appellation of FRCS – Fellow of the Royal College of Surgeons. These four letters are cherished worldwide, especially in Britain's old colonies. Most of these erstwhile dominions have now won political independence. Many have established their own graduate and postgraduate medical courses and degrees.

Nonetheless, a wistful hankering for the revered FRCS, or in the case of physicians, the MRCP (Member of the Royal College of Physicians), persists… and for good reason. After all, the post-nominal letters FRCS or MRCP translate to acquisition of a lucrative private practice, as the locals adore the colonial hangover of a good old-fashioned British qualification – a hallmark that the person has been at least tempered, if not quite "Made in Britain".

Some aspiring overseas surgeons go even further, acquiring Fellowships from more than one Royal College.

'Mr Sinha, you'd better take your mother to see Dr Asok Banerjee. He's a double FRCS you know,' is a line of conversation not uncommon in the Crystal Room of the Calcutta Club.

Of the two parts of the FRCS, the second or the Final is relatively less taxing. This is because the Finals are essentially clinical, covering the day-to-day practice of patient care.

On the other hand, the first part or Primary is completely different. Here, you are grilled on the basic sciences of anatomy, physiology and pathology – stuff that you did long years ago in the early pre-clinical period at medical school, subjects that were often arid and abstruse, a bit like the Latin and Greek of schooldays.

The Primary FRCS exam in our time was even more of a titanic ordeal. We had to acquire an encyclopaedic knowledge of anatomy, physiology and pathology. It was as though we were preparing to be career anatomists, physiologists or pathologists and not clinicians, for whom a concise grasp for safe clinical practice would suffice.

It was as if a prospective tourist for Italy was being asked to master Gibbon's entire *Decline and Fall of the Roman Empire* before being permitted an entry visa.

Nowadays, a more rational approach of including only practical relevant aspects of the basic sciences in the examination curriculum has softened the torment.

In earlier days, the pass rate for the Finals was usually about 25 per cent. For the Primary this fell to a cruel 15 per cent.

In fact, a story, perhaps not entirely apocryphal, describes a council meeting of one of the great Royal

Colleges. An agenda item proposed to restrict the number of attempts at the Primary to no more than four. The resolution was about to be put to the vote, when the President of the Royal College put his hand up. He said that before the honourable council members went ahead and cast their votes, the President wished to make it known that if the resolution were to be passed, he would have to resign on moral grounds. In hushed silence, he confided of his own five attempts!

The already appalling success rate worsened as you descended the candidate pecking order, from home grown graduates of medical schools in the United Kingdom, to overseas doctors from the erstwhile British Empire. Moreover, it was this latter pool that comprised the vast majority of applicants.

Three times a year, a multitude of examination candidates would descend on the four cities of the British Isles that house the Royal Colleges – London, Edinburgh, Glasgow and Dublin.

Many of the candidates, given the poor success rate, would be repeat visitors.

In order to accommodate these several hundreds of young and sadly, sometimes not so young, men and women, many a modest boarding house had sprung up in vicinities close to the Royal Colleges. The length of stay in these lodgings varied. Both exams, Primary and Finals, were in two separate segments – an initial written, comprising essay and multiple choice questions, and a subsequent oral interrogation. If you failed the written, your stay was commensurately short. On the other hand, if you'd done well at the written and had your hopes raised by being invited to submit for the orals, you stayed longer.

The owner-managers of these establishments were, in most part, genial folk with kind hearts, who took your money, looked after you, and in many instances, put a consoling arm around your shoulder over a cup of tea or something stronger. Often you got to know them well from previous visits. Some lodgings even acquired reputations for being lucky... this approbation being strictly applied if more of the chaps who stayed there passed their exams!

When I took the Primary FRCS, I was a young senior house surgeon in orthopaedics at Mount Gould Hospital, Plymouth. I had worked hard in preparation – ploughed through the textbooks, peered down the microscope at pathology slides, and on many a sunny south Devon afternoon, had disappointed my four-year-old son and his little sister by cloistering myself with an articulated skeleton and R. J. Last's textbook of regional anatomy in the hospital's medical education centre.

I relearned and rememorised the anatomical minutiae of the nail bed, the oxygen dissociation curve, each and every cranial nerve that exited the numerous foramina at the base of the skull, the life cycle of some exotic parasite that caused guinea-worm disease...

Soon enough, the time came to send off the cheque for payment of examination fees, book my coach fare (rather than train, to save money) and head off from picturesque Devon to cooler western Scotland. For good measure, I made similar bookings for Dublin, in case success eluded my first attempt in Glasgow.

The boarding house where I stayed in Glasgow was

a simulacrum of other such establishments, as I have described. The owner, however, was different. She was short and round. Her prim white hair had a tinge of dark blue, suggestive of cheap dye. She spoke in a loud rasping voice that grated.

Her opening line was, 'I've been rrunning this business for many years noww. They all know me at the Royal College, all yer grand prefessers and examiners.'

As a special bit of icing, she added, 'Och, and I'm telling you noww – I do nott allow no nonsense in my place.'

She delivered this, standing arms akimbo, on the doorstep, with me outside holding my suitcase, bareheaded under a late November night.

Having risen at dawn for the journey from a corner in south-west England, all the way to Scotland, shouldering the worry of exams, already beginning to miss my young family left behind in hospital accommodation at Plymouth, my shell-shocked brain couldn't care less. I was not quite sure what exactly she meant by 'nonsense'. Was it drink, was it trying to sneak in a woman of ill-repute, was it something worse, like drugs? We were of the swinging sixties generation, after all.

Other indignities followed. At breakfast, she separated and segregated us, the overseas junior doctors, from her few white British clients.

She offered no face-saving explanation. Instead, she twisted the knife.

'I've got to look after my rregular British folk,' she said, as though sitting at the same table as us would contaminate the 'regular British folk'.

She chose not to tidy up after the previous guests from

105

tables to which we were herded. Bits of eggshell and grains of salt and pepper were left uncleared on the cheap paper covering our breakfast table.

I ignored all these petty humiliations with single-minded – indeed dogged – resolve. I focused on the far more important task of getting through the written and MCQ part of the Primary.

Two days later, I walked to the College to collect an envelope. There were many young men and women lounging in the great hall with open envelopes. Several had glum faces. I tore mine open – to my utter relief, I found a slip of paper bearing a terse sentence instructing me to attend the following day for the orals.

I telephoned my wife in Plymouth and celebrated with a double cheeseburger with fries and strawberry milkshake at the nearest MacDonald's.

That evening before the Vivas, I heard raised voices outside my room. As I looked down from the landing, I could see an exchange in the entrance hall. Our worthy landlady was "welcoming" a new entrant. After she'd hectored him about the rules of the house, she delivered her oft-repeated, well-rehearsed admonition of not allowing no nonsense in her house.

To my surprise and to my untrammelled delight, this time she was met with a fitting riposte. In the unmistakable muscular tones of the Punjab, the land of the five rivers and the home of India's "martial race", the tall, square-shouldered, blue-turbaned young Sikh informed our oppressor, 'I've come to do exaam, naht to do nahnsense.'

For once the termagant was flummoxed. Her open mouth emitted only a whimper. I silently applauded.

*

The next day I took my Vivas. A twinkle-eyed professor complimented me on my knowledge of pathology and expressed admiration of the quality of teaching back home at the Medical College, Calcutta. The youngish sandy-haired examiner at the physiology table gave me a conspiratorial wink and said that my one wrong answer wouldn't be counted as the bell had gone before I'd given the incorrect response! The bearded gentleman who asked me to identify the blood vessels and nerves of the pickled forearm in the anatomy glass jar nodded in approval with each correct answer.

That same evening, I packed my case. The bill had been paid in advance, and I didn't have to face my tormentor again to wish her an insincere farewell. I went straight to the coach station to take the overnight National Express back home to Plymouth.

The next morning, I shut the bedroom door of our tiny hospital apartment and asked Mary, the switchboard operator, to place a long distance call for me.

A cheerful young woman with a soft rhotic accent answered. She asked for my roll number and checked the spelling of my full name… she proceeded to speak words of joy.

I put down the telephone and turned my gaze heavenward.

Silently, with blurred eyes, I tore up the papers for Dublin.

CHAPTER 11

Who Will Feed the Camel?

From the Institute of Urology in London to the Great
Pyramids of Giza – 1987

The 1987 Annual World Congress of Endo-Urology (keyhole surgery of the urinary tract) was being held in Cairo.

The Egyptians have always had a reputation for excellence in urology. The prevalence of bilharzia, a water-borne parasitic infection of the urinary tract provides an abundance of clinical material for Egyptian urological surgeons, whose heritage dates back to ancient times as recorded by Herodotus and depicted in the stone bas-reliefs of the necropolis at Saqqara.

The University Hospital at Mansoura attracts surgeons from all over the world for specialist training in highly skilled procedures of bladder and urethral reconstruction. The faculty professors demonstrate how segments of intestine can be used to replace parts destroyed by disease or injury.

Thus the elderly man who's lost his bladder to an aggressive cancer can have a new one fashioned from of a segment of bowel. Similarly, the tearful young woman with remorseless attacks of interstitial cystitis, brought to the edge of despair by the knife of pain deep in her pelvis, having to rush to the toilet every twenty minutes, can have her bladder expanded by patching a suitable flap of small intestine to the shrunken bladder, thereby relieving her symptoms.

I was eager to attend the World Congress; two of my academic papers had been accepted for presentation. At the time, I was thirty-seven and a lecturer at our own British centre of excellence – the Institute of Urology in London.

I was also looking forward to my first visit to Egypt, ancient land of the Pharaohs and the Great Pyramids of Giza.

*

From an overcast drizzly Heathrow, I arrived in Cairo by a comfortable less-than-five-hour BA flight. The hot air hit my face like a blast from a fan heater as I emerged from Cairo's bustling international airport. A short taxi ride saw me ensconced in the new Hilton Semiramis. Viewed from my tenth-floor room, the Nile was in the evening sunset, a gunmetal ribbon with boats and dhows making lazy progress, the bridges and riverside roads teeming with young and old, scrawny dogs and mutely laden donkeys, darting bikes, battered cars and swollen buses belching black diesel fumes.

By the time I had unpacked and showered, I was ready for dinner at the hotel's open-air restaurant.

*

In the days before the end of the Cold War, dollar-rich visitors from the West were eagerly welcomed in places like Egypt and India, even Communist Eastern Europe.

Only the year before, a group of us were in Prague for a urology research conference. We'd gone off for an evening drink at the Hemingway bar and had lost track of time. It was near midnight when we realised that we were famished and decided to go into the nearest hotel in Wenceslas Square, where a somewhat superior young manager in an ill-fitting suit and thin tie told us, 'Sorry sir, restaurant's now closed.'

Despite our collective and bibulous remonstrance, he remained implacable.

At this point, Julian, senior lecturer at the Institute, and our group leader, had the presence of mind to casually take out a wad of greenbacks. The young Czech's (or was he Slovak?) eyes widened.

'Please wait a moment sir,' he said in a hurry.

In less than fifteen minutes, the door to the restaurant was thrown open, the cook and waiters had been roused. The aroma of fried onions presaged the arrival of platters bearing freshly grilled steaks. The manager himself uncorked bottles of very drinkable Riesling.

This time, here in Cairo as well, the maître d' at the Semiramis restaurant displayed commensurate hospitality. He was so pleased to see me, a British guest, that post dinner, he produced a secret bottle of cognac covered with a white towel, and though demurring that he was giving me 'just a *little*,' pronounced '*likkel*', poured a generous measure at no extra cost – an act that, had he been observed and reported by an unsympathetic hardliner, would have earned him more than a rebuke in a strictly Islamic country.

*

The four-day endo-urology conference included a busy programme. I presented my research paper on enzyme changes after shock wave treatment of kidney stones and a clinical paper on minimally invasive surgery, at packed sessions and fielded questions from the international audience.

When the conference was over, I had one remaining day for sightseeing before returning to England.

I chose to spend the day at Giza.

I had already glimpsed the Pyramids on this visit. Late evening of the second day, I'd taken the city coach tour. The last leg of the excursion, and by this time it was nightfall, took us on a route from where the Pyramids could be seen at a distance. It was full moon and my first sight of this wonder of the ancient world was nothing like the golden isosceles of touristy picture postcards. In the lambent moonlight, the Pyramids appeared as black brooding megaliths. As I stood gaping at the roadside, I could feel the hairs on the nape of my neck... was it just a passing desert breeze or really the searing breath of Cheops and Snefaru?

The hotel had booked a taxi on the morning of my full-day visit to Giza. The cab driver Rashid was a jaunty young man, smartly dressed in dark blue jeans and cream polo shirt. A strong smell of deodorant pervaded the interior of the taxi. He had a reasonable smattering of English and an easy manner.

We soon fell into conversation.

'You come on holiday?'

'No, I'm here for a conference.'

'You doktore?'

'Yes, I'm a surgeon.'

After a brief exchange on how well-off, most doctors, especially surgeons, in Cairo were, Rashid offered advice on how to get the most out of my one day at a heritage site where hundreds of tourists jostled for the best picture shot.

'Taxi no can go close to Pyramid.'

Rashid explained that taxis were not permitted to go right up to the Pyramids. That a fair distance had to be covered which would be too long and too uncomfortable in the crucifying heat to cover by foot.

He took his eye off the road, looked into the rear-view mirror and flashed a toothy grin.

'Good for you to take camel ride.'

'Really?' I said.

'Yes, yes. I know very good camel man. He my cousin.'

I hesitated.

'My cousin take you very near Pyramid. He no charge you too much.'

I thought, *OK*, perhaps this could be fun. The image of Peter O'Toole in the glare of the desert, cutting a dashing figure on camelback in *Lawrence of Arabia* sprang to mind.

Rashid assured me that his cousin would be happy with the reasonable sum of fifteen Egyptian pounds.

Ali, his cousin, turned out to be much older, in his late sixties, short in stature, though sturdy despite his age. Unlike Rashid spruced up in a Western outfit, Ali wore the traditional flowing *gallabiyah* of Egyptian men and had a grubby turban tightly wound round his head.

With one hand he held the halter, leading a scrofulous camel with the enchanting name of Amina. After a short loud conversation with Rashid in Kalashnikov-rapid Arabic, Ali helped me mount the camel. I perched on a hard wooden saddle covered with a thin tatty seat cloth. The saddle had a rigid pommel in front to clutch and a smaller one digging uncomfortably into the small of my back to keep me in place and provide purchase on my precarious seat.

It soon became apparent that despite her endearing name, Amina was reluctant to carry anyone, anywhere. She constantly chewed cud and at every opportunity dipped and bucked on the undulating desert surface. Each time she lowered herself with the suddenness of an aeroplane in turbulence, I had to tighten my grip on the front pommel with both hands for fear of being flung off or impaling myself on the rear spur.

Being a urologist, I was all the more conscious of the damage to the urethra that could be sustained in such an awkward jolt. Recalling my school-day lessons on medieval English history, I was also well aware that William the Conqueror had met his end not in battle, but from a similar injury whilst on a hard horseback ride in his native Normandy.

All the time during my perilous ride, Ali kept up a patter of conversation.

'Wilkum. From where you come?'

'London,' I replied.

'Aah, Eenglish, Breetish,' Ali said happily, ignoring my evident Indian appearance. 'Wilkum... wilkum to Egypt.'

Several more 'wilkums' were thrown in for good measure, which failed to distract me from my scary camel ride. I was thankful that it was a mere hundred yards from the taxi rank to the Pyramids. It was also clear at the end of the journey that Rashid's apparently helpful suggestion of the camel ride was just a ploy to further bilk the unsuspecting tourist.

I dismounted with relief, but couldn't bring myself to pat Amina's scabrous back as she continued to chew cud.

I handed Ali the agreed fare, and added, what I considered, was a generous tip of an extra five Egyptian pounds.

Ali looked at the smudged banknotes with knitted brows. His face darkened. He became agitated, and began waving his arms as if to summon an army of djinns. The 'wilkums' dried up and imprecations in rustic Arabic were muttered.

'This no good,' he protested.

'Excuse me?' I tried.

'This money... no enough,' he said shaking the banknotes in his fist, about six inches from my nose.

'Sorry, this is what I agreed with Rashid... your cousin.'

He shook his head with vigour, almost dislodging the grimy turban, 'No good, no enough.'

I held my ground, remained silent and prepared to walk away.

Ali's clinching argument followed — 'Who will feed the kammel?'

As I resolutely turned away and walked ahead to join the throng of sightseers, his parting shot was aimed at my disappearing back —

'Pakkistanni!'

In that fleeting moment, while the dazzling majesty of the Great Pyramids shimmered in the horizon, I plummeted down Ali's tourist pecking order, and his gobbet of spittle hit the burning desert sand.

CHAPTER 12

St Peter's, the Colonel and the Savoy

St Peter's Hospital for Stone, The Institute of Urology,
London – 1989

St Peter's location on 27 Henrietta Street, WC1, in the heart of Covent Garden, clearly lent its own charm to those of us fortunate to have worked in that centre of international repute, more so when we lived in, whilst on-call.

You pulled open the hospital's black-painted high front door with its polished brass knob, and stepped straight into a bright world of cafes, artisan pubs, flower stalls, bookshops, and boutique stores.

Opposite the hospital, one could glimpse through tinted glass panes diners clinking champagne flutes, sitting at tables covered with crisp white linen, inside Rules, the upscale West End restaurant with a sumptuary menu that included game, complemented by an oenophile's cellar.

Having emerged on the busy pavement of Henrietta Street, going left would lead you to Covent Garden Market. From here, you could go down Southampton Street, and in less than a hundred yards, come upon the Strand. As soon as you had taken in the pedestrian bustle and the whizz of fast-moving traffic on the dual carriageway, the most arresting sight ahead, that lifted your gaze, was the palatial Savoy, the iconic London luxury hotel, with the attached theatre of the same name.

I was senior registrar in urology at the time of this story in 1989, which links St Peter's with the Savoy.

The three specialist London hospitals for the exclusive treatment of urinary diseases were St Peter's, St Paul's and St Phillip's, collectively known as the "three Ps". Along with another specialist urology hospital, the Shaftesbury, which housed the group's medical library and academic unit for research, all four unique hospitals were situated in snug proximity to Covent Garden Market and the Royal Opera House.

Together, they comprised the renowned Institute of Urology. In those days, the Institute was the tertiary referral centre for all the major sub-specialties in urology - oncology, urinary stones, kidney transplantation, reconstructive surgery and andrology. The clinical and academic staff at the Institute were *the* best in the United Kingdom. We were the Oxbridge of British urology.

The Institute's andrology clinic was based at St Peter's outpatients.

*

Andrology, a subspecialty of urology, is the art and science of treating male sexual disorders. During the early 1980s, when I started training in urology after passing my final FRCS exam, andrology was not as yet a major branch of urology, although things were changing.

Unlike the established section specialties, andrology was merely the new kid on the block. Compared to cancer and kidney failure, male sexual inadequacy was considered just a distraction.

Rhodri Price-Thomas FRCS, a consultant surgeon in Wales from my early training years, related a story from the hoary past, of indifference towards men who "dared" complain of sexual problems.

We'd just finished a long clinic, it was late evening and most of the outpatient staff had gone home. Much needed tea appeared, in cups and saucers rattling on a tray. My consultant leaned back on his chair, lacing his hands at the back of his head.

'As I said earlier, I was a trainee like you, except we were called surgical dressers in those days. I was working in London. My boss was this knighted Harley Street surgeon. I remember one of his patients, a big chap, who'd come to clinic for follow-up. He'd had a prostatectomy… and bear in mind, in those days, a prostate op wasn't a walk in the park. There was no keyhole surgery – you made this huge slash in the lower abdomen, and there was usually a bloodbath after you got in and wrenched out the prostate… as you can imagine, a great many just didn't make it after the op.'

Mr Price-Thomas paused to take a sip of his Earl Grey.

'Anyway, outpatients sister brought this man in and sat him down in front of Sir-God-Himself, with us juniors and medical students standing crowded around the great man on his upholstered chair. The boss asked, "I take it you're now passing your water without trouble?" "Yes sir, thank you," the chap said. "Your operation was a miracle… and I'm not up as often at night." "Excellent,

I'm pleased." With that, the chief looked up at sister as if to say, "All done here Sister, let's see the next fellow now." The patient didn't get up though. He hesitated and looked at his hands before he said, "Sir, there's just one thing." "*Yess?*" "It's just that... things down below... they don't seem to work as before.""

Rhodri Price-Thomas chuckled at the recollection. He continued, 'The Master-Surgeon's face was something to see. He went almost apoplectic... glared over his pebble-glasses as though he'd discovered a slug in his garden. His voice was stone cold; I'll never forget those words – "That is of no concern... *get a grip on yourself man*. Good day to you!""

*

By the mid-1980s, the attitude towards erectile problems in men had improved considerably. A better understanding of what caused impotence, a well worked-out pathway of investigative tests, and the discovery of treatments that worked, led to an overall holistic approach and much better care.

John Pryor FRCS was one of our senior consultants at St Peter's. He was another of the Olympians at the Institute of Urology. An original thinker and innovative surgeon, John was a much sought-after keynote speaker at international andrology meetings. Over the years, John had built a worldwide reputation in his specialty. At the Institute, you didn't get appointed to the consultant staff unless you had global recognition.

In 1983, it had been discovered that injecting vasoactive

drugs directly into the penis resulted in a most satisfying erection in men who were experiencing difficulties.

The way it worked was this – for a firm erection, the penis needs to fill with blood to the point of turgidity. When the blood vessels of the penis are damaged such as in diabetes or arteriosclerosis, the penis is inadequately filled, resulting in perhaps some tumescence, but not a rigid erection.

Injection of vasoactive drugs into the penis dilates the blood vessels, which then fill adequately. The drug used was papaverine, an opium alkaloid. It was effective, but not entirely free of problems, especially painful and prolonged erections in some men.

We subsequently discovered that the naturally occurring compound prostaglandin, used in cardiology to keep open narrowed blood vessels, had the potential of providing the same good results but with fewer side-effects.

At St Peter's, we were fine-tuning the dose of prostaglandin that worked best.

*

Friday afternoons, when most people who were not on-call had gone off for the weekend, it was my role as senior registrar to do the andrology clinic with John Pryor and our good-natured, matronly outpatient staff nurse, Jenny.

Outpatients at St Peter's was spacious, taking up nearly the entire left wing of the ground floor. There were a number of consulting rooms with desks and chairs, as well as examination couches.

The initial consultation included taking a full history,

making a note of relevant other medical conditions such as high blood pressure, diabetes, heart disease as well as all medication, and drug allergies.

Thereafter, a physical examination was carried out.

We would also use the same couches to perform the prostaglandin injections into the penis. This may sound painful. However, in reality, carried out with gentleness and empathy, most men did not complain. Many of our patients were diabetics, adept with injecting themselves every day with insulin.

Moreover, we used the finest-gauge orange-coloured needles.

Most men hardly felt the pinpoint puncture, just a warm sensation as the drug solution entered the lacunae of tiny blood vessels, a bit like a hot flush.

The men were then left in the privacy of their individual rooms, as the prostaglandin would take at least ten to fifteen minutes to take effect.

After a decent interval, we would return to check on whether the injection had worked.

The first man in whom we achieved success with prostaglandin was a small diffident Chinese man with a wispy moustache. He was accompanied by his equally tiny wife who spoke little English, but who always smiled and nodded rapidly whenever we asked if they understood what was being done.

Twenty minutes after the Chinese gentleman's injection, when I went in to check, a spike of hard flesh rather than flaccidity greeted me.

I rushed next door to John's office.

'Great result, our man's got a really strong erection.'

John didn't take his eyes off the CT scan that he was studying.

'He's next door if you want to come and see,' I said, breathless with as much excitement as the discovery of penicillin.

John gave me an indulgent look, and said drily, 'One erection's much the same as another!'

*

As an aside, I'm recounting a couple of incidents related to the running of a male sexual health clinic.

The first one was at St Peter's itself. One Friday afternoon, a nice white-haired lady with a slight stoop, replete with plaid handbag, registered at reception as a new referral. She was taken to John's consulting room. I was asked to examine her after we'd taken her medical history.

I escorted our elderly lady, firmly clutching her handbag, to an adjoining examining room, and requested her to undress below the waist while I went out to find a chaperone.

Minutes later, a scream echoed through outpatients. Not knowing that the room was occupied, Jenny had walked in without knocking – she found, lying on the couch, the nice white-haired lady naked below the waist… a familiar appendage confirming that John Pryor had a large practice in trans-gender surgery!

My next escapade took place a couple of years later.

When I came to Croydon as a new consultant, I was asked to set up the andrology service. This obviously included penile injections.

Suitable clinic accommodation was scarce in the main Mayday Hospital. As the newest appointee to the surgical consultant staff, I was sent offsite to do my clinics at Croydon General Hospital, a rundown slate-grey building with no inpatient beds, situated close to tawdry West Croydon rail station.

After much cajoling, I succeeded in convincing the outpatient manager to provide a small room in the basement, away from the busy main clinic on the ground floor. It was actually the room belonging to a young woman ECG technician that I was allowed to use, and only at the specific times when she didn't need it.

I was expected to give the injections down there in the basement, then run up to continue my general urology clinic upstairs.

With the help of Eve, our senior staff nurse, adept at juggling multiple tasks, this worked reasonably well, except the day when the auburn-haired ECG technician walked into her office, having forgotten that this was the injection morning. The young lady did not take kindly to the shock of her unexpected meeting with a recumbent priapic man. The subsequent look that she fired sizzled my eyebrows. I'm sure she would've liked to have reported me and my poxy andrology clinic to the medical director for, at the very least, a stern verbal warning.

*

One of the many patients whose story has left an imprint was Rupert Smythe-Rogers, back at St Peter's.

Rupert was a retired army officer in his early fifties.

He would come to St Peter's outpatients, dressed in dark brown tweed suit and paisley silk tie. His was a tale all too familiar in our andrology clinic.

'Just wasn't getting stiff enough,' he complained. 'At first, I thought it was the stress of the new City job. And I'm not exactly young anymore.'

Concern crept in when the week on a Greek island with his wife failed to reinvigorate their sex life. A descending vortex of misery set in – the initial physical problem and the resultant corrosive worry conspired to inflict on the couple a self-perpetuating vicious cycle.

'Nothing worked, so my wife thought it best to see if the GP could help.'

His general practitioner wrote a sensible referral letter to John Pryor outlining the problem.

Rupert responded well to his first prostaglandin injection. The second, at exactly the same dose, produced a result that was an unqualified success. The improvement from the first injection, almost certainly, was the result of his restored self-confidence.

We agreed to try another prostaglandin injection at a lower dose, before embarking on a course of self-injection, teaching Rupert how to inject himself, as we did for others in whom the injections had worked.

He booked himself in for a return visit the following Friday.

He turned up early for his appointment, mildly reproved me for calling him in from the waiting room as Lieutenant-Colonel Smythe-Rogers – he seemed to prefer the anonymity of plain Mr Rogers. Perhaps he felt that he was letting Sandhurst down, that it wasn't quite cricket for British army officers, even retired ones, to have imperfections, especially sensitive ones such as this.

As before, he looked steadily at the ceiling, his features impassive, while I administered his injection.

'See you shortly,' I said, leaving him in the privacy of the examination room.

Twenty minutes passed quickly. I remembered to go back and check on Rupert. I knocked on the door and went in. To my astonishment the room was empty, the linen on the examination couch was dishevelled, as though the occupant had left in a hurry. We searched all the other rooms, and thereafter, the rest of outpatients – nothing.

His disappearance was a mystery.

The following Friday, Rupert came back, punctual for his appointment. He had a pleased look about him, as though something had gone well recently. There were no clues to his mysterious disappearance the week before.

I called him in and prepared his injection. I asked him why he had left in such a seeming hurry the week before.

'Well Mr Das, you remember the second injection you gave me?'

'Yes, I do.'

'It was brilliant.'

'I know; I remember that you were very happy.'

'Well, I got home really chuffed, but the frustrating thing was that as soon as I got in through the front door, it started going down.'

'I did say that it wouldn't last more than an hour or so, and we didn't want any problems with a prolonged erection.'

'Yes, I remember how emphatic you were.'

'OK, so where did you disappear last week? We were worried.'

A smile wreathed our colonel's countenance, as though he knew that he had got one over me.

'Well, what I did last time was to bring the old girl along. We booked a room in the hotel nearby.'

I listened, fascinated.

'And we've booked a room today as well.'

'Where?' I feebly asked.

'Why, the Savoy of course!'

CHAPTER 13

Mea culpa – Iatrogenic Injuries

St George's Hospital, London – 2009
Shelstone Park Hospital, London – 2004
The Devonshire Clinic, Harley Street – 1986
St Peter's Hospital, Henrietta Street, the Institute
of Urology – 1989

1.

It was cold and dark when I left home at twenty-past six for St George's Hospital on a Tuesday morning in late November. The Mini Cooper's headlights probed a snaking path down Slines Oak Road in Woldingham village to join the main Limpsfield Road in Warlingham. Only on the Old Farleigh Road was there the first sparse pre-dawn traffic.

I sped through Croydon, making good progress through Collier's Wood towards Tooting with a brief halt at the level crossing of Mitcham Eastfields station. Terry Wogan soothed his listeners with easy persiflage on Radio 2 as a Southern Railway train elided past in a blur of white and green. The barriers soon rose, and I joined the flow straight on across the A24 to Blackshaw Road. I drove into St George's main entrance as the sky was lightening. It had just gone 7.15 am. At that hour, there was no difficulty in finding a space in the consultants' car park.

Up one flight of stairs in the St James' wing, I reached the theatre complex. As I touched my identity card with magnetic stripe to the sensor outside the entrance, the soft click presaged disengagement of the electronic lock. I pushed open the set of double doors to find Alberto, the operating theatre manager checking the day's theatre allocation list.

'Morning Mr Das, you're in cardiac theatres today.'

'Oh good, have you seen Emma, or any of the anaesthetic team?'

'Dr Evans has seen your patient and is in the anaesthetic room in cardiac. Your registrar Ben's gone back to the ward to see a patient. He said he wouldn't be long.'

I made my way across the passageway connecting the St James' wing to the Atkinson Morley building where cardiac theatres were located. Eminent surgeons of yesteryear looked down with sideburns and stern appraising expressions from framed portraits. They seemed to ask – 'Are you good enough to walk in our footsteps?' I punched in the four-digit code for the male changing room in cardiac and emerged in blue scrubs and chalk-white theatre boots.

The first case on the operating list was a radical cystectomy. My first assistant that morning was Ben, our SpR (specialist registrar) in his final year of training. Ben had all the qualities as well as the training requisites for shaping into an excellent pelvic cancer surgeon. I was happy to take him through the complex operation, and for him to do as much of the actual surgery as he felt comfortable with.

Radical cystectomy is arguably the most challenging

operation in urology. It is performed with the intention of curing patients with invasive bladder cancer, where the malignant tumour has burrowed into the deep muscle wall of the bladder, hence the term "invasive".

The operation involves cutting out in its entirety, the cancerous urinary bladder along with regional lymph nodes, prostate (in men), uterus (in women) and the full length of the urethra. Having removed the diseased organ, we then have to create a replacement urinary bladder using a segment of small intestine. The ureters are connected to the inner end of this "new" bladder made out of bowel, the other end of which is brought out as an external stoma.

The entire operation can take anything from four to six hours. Even with modern surgical and anaesthetic techniques, along with intensive care backup, radical cystectomy is burdened with a small rate of mortality. Despite all our efforts, some people will not survive this herculean operation.

To perform radical cystectomy well and achieve the best possible outcome for his or her patient, the surgeon must remove much of the contents of the pelvic cavity (as I've said, the whole bladder along with prostate/uterus, lymph nodes and urethra) without losing too much blood - this is the *excisional* part. Thereafter, he needs to do a lot of delicate needlework – the stitching together or *reconstructive* part of the operation, where cut ends of bowel are reconnected in a watertight anastomosis, and the severed ends of the ureters sewn onto the bowel segment that forms the new bladder.

Radical cystectomy therefore comprises two distinct mind-sets of operating.

The first excisional or "cutting out" part focuses on making absolutely sure that all the cancer has been removed. The next reconstructive or "bringing together" part concentrates on creating a new bladder that is secure and watertight. Internal leaks whether of bowel contents or urine are an unmitigated disaster as collections of toxic waste products in the form of faecal matter or urine leads to peritonitis, which if untreated is invariably fatal.

Both segments of radical cystectomy require meticulous care and attention.

The operation started well that morning. We were in Cardiac Theatre 3 of the Atkinson Morley wing of St George's. The cardiac theatres at St George's are a delight to work in. Of relatively new build, you can accommodate a huddle of medical students without feeling hemmed in. The overhead theatre lighting provides brilliant ambient bluish light that illuminates the four walls and reaches distant ceiling corners unlike the yellowing myopic dimness of older theatres. The polished vinyl floor is spruce and business-like. I never dared ask what the cardiac surgeons, whose domain cardiac theatres really were, thought about "foreign" urological cancer surgeons invading their territory, especially a guest surgeon from Croydon!

Ben and I scrubbed up, standing side by side. The gleaming no-touch taps provided streams of warm water. We squirted liberal jets of antiseptic povidone-iodine on the palm of our hands. With soft polythene single-use brushes we worked up a rich foam of orange-brown lather on hands, forearms and elbows. We chatted companionably as we scrubbed.

'So what did you get up to last weekend?' I asked Ben.

'On-call, I'm afraid. Nothing exciting, just the usual urinary retentions, renal colics and a couple of testis torsions. How was your tennis match on Saturday?'

'Great,' I said. 'We managed to hold our own against the registrars. I even got 60 per cent of my first serves in.'

We had been able start the operation early; there'd been no problems in reserving an HDU (high dependency unit) bed for the immediate post-operative period, a common cause for delay. Our consultant anaesthetist Emma had inserted the epidural, central venous and arterial lines while we the surgical team were still swallowing our first cups of coffee. The great thing about Emma was that apart from being an excellent anaesthetist, she was always in good humour even when she would tell us off for our myriad transgressions – putting too many cases on a list, forgetting to check whether an ITU or HDU bed would be available...

Matilda, our scrub nurse had ensured that the Turner-Warwick retractor set that I particularly favoured was available at the outset. Best of all, it was Ben assisting and not a more junior trainee.

I let Ben open the lower abdomen through an incision starting at the level of the belly-button going straight down to just above the pubic bone. We inserted the blades of the Turner-Warwick retractors, sensibly designed with matte black coating, so as not to reflect the bright overhead light and dazzle the operators.

The patient was a slim man in his sixties. We were able get inside the pelvic cavity and start the business side of the complex operation, with minimum time spent on tediously cutting through the skin and external layers. We started clearing the lymph nodes from the pelvic side wall and dissecting out the bladder. The lymph node dissection involved clearing fatty tissue off the finger-thick blood vessels in the vicinity, the iliac arteries and veins. Absolute focus and concentration is required as one is working with sharp instruments at very close proximity to these large blood vessels, which are unforgiving if disrespected.

Ben did a beautiful dissection on his side of the pelvis. As I took over for my side, and whilst under-running a small blood vessel, I managed to prang the external iliac vein with the tip of a curved needle. Fortunately, this was a relatively delicate 3/0 round-bodied needle rather than a large cutting needle, which would have caused a rent in the vein and not just a pinprick. Nonetheless, an angry surge of venous blood chased after the offending needle tip. I was able to quickly put pressure on the puncture with a swab-on-holder that Matilda had promptly held out for me.

With a few minutes of firm pressure, the bleeding stopped. It could have been worse. This was a minor reversible setback, which apart from adding an extra few minutes, was inconsequential and did not have any adverse effect on our patient. Even so, it wasn't part of the script, the patient had not asked for this digression.

This episode is a trivial example of what in surgical jargon is termed iatrogenic injury, or unintentional doctor-inflicted injury.

Every busy surgeon will have his fair share of unintentional mishaps in theatres. As a first-year trainee, I had perforated an elderly lady's thin-walled bladder while resecting a cancer recurrence with the electric wire-loop of an operating resectoscope. As a senior registrar, I had made a perforation in the ureter when, against better judgement, I'd used the more powerful electrohydraulic mode of energy to break up a small ureteric stone when the pulsed dye laser had packed up. As a senior consultant, I was shocked to see my first tear of the rectum while performing radical cystectomy on a woman whose tissue planes were stuck down by previous radiotherapy and the scarring of an earlier hysterectomy. It was all the more galling as I had by then performed close to one hundred of these complex major operations.

As a urological surgeon I have assisted colleagues in other specialties in their hour of need. Gynaecologists have called upon me to repair ureters and bladders unintentionally damaged in the course of difficult hysterectomy or in the presence of endometriosis, which knots down flesh and obliterates normal tissue planes, making it difficult to carry out safe dissection.

In situations of iatrogenic injury, apart from early recognition and appropriate corrective action, it is a *sine qua non* (an absolute imperative) that at the earliest opportune moment, the patient is provided with a full explanation in an open, transparent and sensitive manner. Most people recognise that even doctors and surgeons make mistakes. Most individuals do not hold grudges and are generally forgiving. Of course, a modicum of initial recrimination or anger is sometimes inevitable and understandable.

The radical cystectomy at St George's that morning thereafter progressed uneventfully. We finished in good time. There had been no further significant blood loss. We didn't even need to transfuse any of the six units stored for the operation in the blood bank. The playful smile on Emma's face was a tick on the plus side of my ledger.

Having checked that all was well with my patient, now safely recovering in HDU, I drove home to Woldingham as the winter evening drew in. At Collier's Wood, the homebound traffic slowed my Mini to a standstill. As with every other surgeon, I went over the day's operating in my head. The iatrogenic vein prick had been a minor mishap, inconsequential to the eventual outcome. Nonetheless, I felt annoyed with myself, a niggle that persisted and set off a train of thought.

2.

A few years earlier, I had stood at the nursing desk of the first floor ward of Shelstone Park Hospital, to face the full wrath of a young woman's incandescent father, who'd been called at work to be warned that his daughter Rachel had suffered a complication during a seemingly routine diagnostic laparoscopy performed by a gynaecology consultant.

I had been summoned to repair the iatrogenic ureteric injury, which required a reconstructive operation – trimming the damaged lower end of ureter and reimplanting it into a specially created flap of bladder. The operation to repair the injured ureter goes by the esoteric name of Boari-Ockerblad flap. The additional surgery to mend the unintended damage had added an extra hour-plus to the original twenty-minute laparoscopy.

At the end of the now much longer procedure, while my gynaecology colleague closed up, I went to meet Rachel's father who was waiting to find out what was going on.

I walked straight from theatres towards the first floor ward, still in my blue scrubs and operating boots. As I walked down the passageway and turned into the ward corridor, I saw in the distance a burly 6 ft-something man standing at the nurses' station in the middle of the ward. As I neared, I could see that the red-faced, early-fiftyish man was drumming his fingers on the raised nursing desk. He too had seen me, and immediately locked eyes. He kept up this hard stare all the time it took me to walk the full 15 yards to him as I consciously stopped myself from hurrying and thereby giving the impression of guilty contrition.

His expression forbade proffering a handshake.

'Mr Adams, sorry to have kept you waiting. I'm Gautam Das, consultant urologist. Your daughter's absolutely fine now.'

'So what went wrong?'

'Happy to explain fully. OK if we go and sit in sister's office?'

'No, you can say what you've got to say right here.'

I explained that my gynaecology colleague had encountered adhesions from widespread pelvic endometriosis that had muddied the tissue planes. This was a factor in the injury to the ureter while attempting to take a biopsy of nearby pelvic tissue. The injury had been recognised straightaway and the gynaecologist had called me in. Between the two of us, the problem had been sorted and Rachel would not suffer any long-term complication.

Whilst I spoke, the man's smouldering gaze moved from my eyes, up to the top of my theatre cap, then down to a point somewhere at the centre of my chest, and then back again to my face. He kept doing this all the time I spoke. It was as though he was with great difficulty, restraining himself from saying something vitriolic, or even throwing a punch.

The moment I paused, a pent-up tirade followed.

'This should never have happened. Mr Torrington didn't mention *any* of this when we met him in the consulting room. He should've been *much* more careful.'

Imprecations followed. I was advised in no uncertain terms, that the last had not been said on the matter.

Rachel herself, a bubbly young woman in her early-twenties, with flaxen hair and hazel eyes, took it all in her stride. She cheerfully put up with the catheter that I had to put in while her bladder healed. Her youthful smile uplifted us when she came back a week later to have her catheter and ureteric stent removed. We saw no more of her father. Perhaps Rachel had calmed him down.

No solicitor's letter landed on our desk.

3.

Other memories included the elderly lady in a private Harley Street clinic. This was during my research year at the Institute of Urology. In our training times during the 1980s, a period of research was essential for a young man or woman to get on towards that all-important senior registrar post, the final hurdle before at last reaching the cloud-piercing summit for that ultimate prize – a consultant appointment.

Research was also fun. One learned new things – you went back to the basic sciences and acquired skills in the laboratory. I soon learned that putting my trays of carefully grown bladder cancer cells in the wrong section of the refrigerator cabinet would contaminate the petri dishes, resulting in a whole week's painstaking work being irretrievably lost!

The single disadvantage of the research period was a pecuniary one. Because you were not on-call, you didn't earn the extra UMTs (units of medical time), those essential accretions to basic salary that were so necessary for junior doctors with young families and school-going children.

In order to make up for the deficit, most of us would work extra hours at day's end. Many of us did evening and night sessions at accident & emergency, enduring a lumpen brigade, usually bellicose and invariably inebriated, who had a penchant for the late hours in any A&E up and down the country.

In central London, the plentiful availability of locum work as RMOs (resident medical officers) in the private hospitals and clinics provided a more varied opportunity. A group of us working at the Institute of Urology and other London teaching hospitals in research jobs clubbed together to provide such a service to a set of West End private establishments. Although the range of afflictions were the same as in the NHS, there existed interesting variations in the delivery and practice of medical care, as indeed with the personalities of the patients themselves.

Many were from the Arabian Peninsula with sacks full of petrodollars. The Iranian government sent their badly burned young soldiers, victims of the prolonged fratricidal Iran-Iraq conflict. Despite their disfigurements and the prospect of several plastic surgeries, the men, many still teenagers, never lost their youthful exuberance. In contrast, a crotchety English baronet insisted with a testy thrust of his forefinger that I insert his title in the consent form for his haemorrhoid operation!

An elderly lady with a silver-handled cane and pearl brooch was due to spend an afternoon in one of these plush private clinics to have her system re-energised by a special liquid concoction of vitamins, hormones and assorted nutrients. The Harley Street consultant had left instructions that the pint of light-amber fluid was to be slowly transfused by the intravenous route. As the duty RMO, it was my job to carry out the venepuncture and set up the transfusion of this magical elixir.

The only problem was that she had terrible veins. There were none to be seen in her plump forearm or the saggy folds in the crook of her elbow. The only visible veins were on the back of her hand and those too looked spidery and uncooperative. The first puncture found a vein. However, the lady's sharp withdrawal with a shrill 'Oooh' at the needle-prick resulted in dislodgement of the cannula and a small spillage of dark blood.

Once the assisting nurse and I had both apologised, a second attempt was cautiously undertaken having applied a further blob of local anaesthetic gel on the skin surface.

This time the needle tip stayed in place. I gently pushed in the fine-bore clear plastic cannula and withdrew the needle. The nurse connected up the transfusion line. We both breathed a silent sigh of relief. Unfortunately, as soon as the viscous fluid trickled in, the fragile vein ballooned and leaked. A blue blob quickly formed on the desiccated skin.

The lady was not amused.

'This is awful. I did *not* come to Harley Street to be used as a pincushion. Where's Dr Buckman?'

She refused further ministration and insisted on seeing the consultant. Competence was questioned and I heard the word complaint several times.

4.

A happier reminiscence took me back to St Peter's Hospital when I was senior registrar. The Institute of Urology had a large referral base for complex male sexual and genital problems. One of the conditions commonly referred to us was Peyronie's disease. This is a disorder of the penis where on erection, the penis bends in an acute curve, usually upwards and sometimes to one or other side. The effect is that sexual penetration is difficult and painful, and in advanced stages, impossible. The effect of this debility on relationships can be devastating.

It is not definitely known what causes this disabling condition, which was first described by the Paris surgeon Francois Peyronie in 1743, when he was Royal Surgeon to the dazzling court of Louis XV, great-grandson and successor of the Sun King Louis XIV.

What we do know for certain about Peyronie's disease is that the deformity of the penis is caused by formation of inelastic scar tissue in the tough fibrous sheath, known as the *tunica albuginea*, which encases the two cylinders of spongy erectile tissue of the penis.

During erection, sexual arousal sends off nerve signals that release potent chemicals. These neurotransmitters relax the delicate smooth muscle lattice of the spongy erectile tissue, thereby allowing the cylinders to fill with blood till the tunica stretches and expands to a rigid erection, similar to pumping air into a bicycle tyre stretching the rubber till the tyre is firm.

In Peyronie's, the scar tissue tethers down the tunica at the point where it has formed, and as the scarring is most often on the dorsal or upper surface of the penis, the curved penis points upwards. There is historical record that the Byzantine Emperor Heraclitus had such a bent penis that it caused him to urinate on his face!

Fortunately, in most men the condition does not progress to complete inability of sexual intercourse, and only about 10 per cent of sufferers require corrective surgery. The operation that was popular in the 1980s was described by an American urologist by the name of Reed Nesbit. In this operation, a scar is deliberately created on the opposite side of the existing "disease" scar. The idea is that this surgeon-created scar balances the existing disease scar thereby straightening the penis.

The operation of creating the balancing scar involves carefully dissecting the urethra off the under surface of the tunica albuginea, and thereafter, snipping off a sliver of the tunica and closing the small gap with fine monofilament nylon sutures. As with any operation, there is a complication rate, which includes inadvertent damage to the urethra.

As part of my senior registrar training, I had been taught how to carry out this procedure and had performed several independently.

It was a routine afternoon list at St Peter's that I had been entrusted with. The last case was a Nesbit correction of Peyronie's. The operation started uneventfully and I was gently dissecting the urethra off the tunica using a small 15 blade scalpel. I must have momentarily gone into the wrong tissue plane for I suddenly found myself with a small but definite nick in the urethra with the lumen clearly visible.

I felt absolutely awful. I thought it best not go any further with the operation other than to close the small opening in the urethra with fine sutures and insert a catheter to "rest" the healing urethra. With leaden heart, I did this and then closed the skin incision of the penis.

At the end of the list, I went to Long ward, our male section at St Peter's, to check on the patients that I'd operated on. Paul, the man whose urethra I had injured was resting comfortably, eyes closed, dozy from the anaesthetic.

Still downhearted, I went to the Institute library at the nearby Shaftesbury Hospital to look up complications of Nesbit correction of Peyronie's. Although urethral injury was a recognised complication, the incidence was relatively low. This made me feel even worse. My boss, John Pryor, senior consultant and an authority on andrology, the specialty of male sexual disorders, was working in his office when I went up for my confessional.

To my relief, I was not berated or rebuked. John acquiesced with the further plan of treatment including re-operation once the urethra had healed. The support that I received that afternoon was heartening and memorable.

The same evening, I went back to Long ward to explain the mishap to Paul.

I'd first met Paul Struthers, a draughtsman in his early fifties from Dorset when he had come up all the way from a village outside Weymouth for his consultation. I had gained his confidence and that of his wife when I'd made the diagnosis, explained the condition and reassured the couple that the deformity was correctable and that their love life was not at an end.

He was sitting up in bed having fully recovered from the anaesthetic. A dinner tray with a gravy-smeared plate was still on his lap. I pulled up a chair beside his bed, sat down and made a clean breast of the situation. Paul did not interrupt even once during my narrative.

'I'm very sorry at what's happened. I'm also sorry that we'll have to wait a couple of weeks. The urethra has to heal before we can do the op again.'

I wouldn't have been surprised if there'd been annoyance, anger, recrimination.

Instead Paul's countenance softened further.

'These things happen Doc. You just had a bad day. You should see what the lads get up to in the factory,' he said. 'I need this op whatever.'

'I promise you, this time I'll make sure that the boss does it himself.'

'Don't mind if he's around, but I still want *you* to do it.'

CHAPTER 14

57 Woodcroft Road

Hospital accommodation in Woodcroft Road, near Mayday Hospital, Thornton Heath, Croydon – 1990

The sound of a telephone ringing at 3am is never welcome.

I reached for the handset and answered before my wife was woken.

'Mr Das, Mayday Hospital switchboard here. Sorry to bother you at this hour – ITU wants a word.'

There was a brief pause.

'Mr Das, this is Chris, surgical registrar. I'm calling about the patient you have in ITU.'

By this time, I was fully awake, alert and sitting up.

'I do not have a patient in ITU,' I said firmly.

Chris, a registrar in one of the general surgery firms, said that the man whose radical nephrectomy I had done in the afternoon had been transferred from the urology ward to ITU just after midnight.

The benefit of being jolted awake by a call about a post-operative patient is the flash of instant recall. All the clinical details tumbled into my conscious mind – the patient was a sixty-seven-year-old man who had a big 8 cm cancerous mass in the upper pole of his left kidney. Frederick Carston had been previously fit and well. His cancer had been diagnosed on CT scan carried out to see why he was passing fresh blood in the urine.

The nephrectomy to remove his cancerous left kidney had taken about two hours, which is the average time for this operation. I'd struggled a bit while dissecting the top part of the kidney, from where the tumour had grown, but had been able to find and ligate the main renal artery and renal vein without difficulty. This is the critical part of the operation where things can go horribly wrong. If either of these large blood vessels are not properly identified, carefully dissected out and securely tied before cutting, an instantaneous bloodbath follows.

The registrar went on to tell me that having been fine in the immediate post-op period and all evening, with hardly any blood coming out of the internal drain, Mr Carston's blood pressure had started to drop around 11pm. The on-call surgical team had speeded up his intravenous fluids and had started blood transfusion.

Despite this, the blood pressure had continued to fall, though there was still no bleeding from the drain. The night surgical team had arranged for the patient to be transferred to intensive care.

All this had been done *without anyone informing me*, the consultant surgeon who had performed the operation!

*

No surgeon wishes his patient to suffer complications from surgery, least of all a potentially fatal one. We didn't go to medical school, and put ourselves, and our families, through all those years of training to do more harm than good. It is only the most egregious who can be dispassionate to suffering, especially if they are the cause, however unintentional.

Moreover, as professionals, we take pride in our work, and good results are the ultimate yardstick of ability and safe surgical practice. Furthermore, for the newly appointed, with an as yet unproven track record, it is all the more important to avoid mishaps, especially lethal ones. A serious complication is a disaster. In cricketing analogy, this would be akin to a promising opener being clean bowled for a duck in the very first over of his maiden Test match.

*

It was my first year as a newly appointed consultant urological surgeon, and no longer a trainee. The ultimate responsibility for patient care lay, with unequivocal firmness, at my doorstep.

Although it rankled that I hadn't been called much earlier, I knew, having been a junior hospital doctor myself till only a few months ago, that in those days, a prevailing culture of hierarchy meant that junior doctors were loath to bother the chief with out-of-hours problems.

Moreover, there was also the apprehension felt by registrars higher up the training ladder, of being considered lacking in competence and confidence, if they called the consultant too early and too often. This accusation, real or imagined, could reflect badly in the confidential reference provided by the consultant on the registrar's ability. A poor reference would inevitably blight the trainee's chances of obtaining the next job up the career tree.

For many years now, the unsatisfactory situation outlined above has vastly improved. Trainees are far better supported and mentored by their seniors, and are encouraged and expected to call for help much sooner. I often get calls directly from ward nurses and the most junior of hospital doctors, the delightful house officers who arrive in fresh blooms from medical schools every February and August, and are now known by their modern terminology, as FY1s or Foundation Year 1 doctors.

*

'I'm afraid, he isn't doing very well,' Chris continued. 'We're trying our best, but I thought I'd let you know that it doesn't look very hopeful...'

I interrupted. 'Listen Chris, I want you to take this man to theatres immediately. Inform the anaesthetists that I'll explore. Do it right now. I'm just round the corner from Mayday in Woodcroft Road. I'll be with you in ten minutes.'

I dressed quickly, with a fleeting glance at my sleeping wife. As I hurried downstairs, Pebbles and Bruno, our two Labradors, lying curled on the landing carpet, looked at me without enthusiasm. They knew it was too early for their morning run. I quietly released the latch on the front door, and came out of the terraced house on 57 Woodcroft Road, temporarily provided by the hospital whilst we were house-hunting. I stepped into the night air of a deserted Thornton Heath, West Croydon.

With footsteps eating up the pathway, I passed other similar terraced houses and within a few minutes came to the Woodcroft Road entrance, the rear portal of Mayday. I strode past the consultants' car park on my left, at this hour desolate, apart from the on-call anaesthetist and the duty obstetrician's cars, and entered the old Woodcroft wing of the hospital.

I raced up a flight of stairs, briskly crossed the long corridor to the new surgical wing, bounded up another flight of stairs and was inside the brightly lit lobby of main theatres. I hadn't been delayed by umpteen locked doors and having to correctly punch in all the different four-digit security combinations as I would now.

I swiftly changed into blue theatre scrubs in the male locker room, again in those trustful days, without the need to unlock a security clasp.

In Theatre 2, I was relieved to see that it was Dr Navaratnarajah, our experienced senior consultant anaesthetist, who was on-call that night, still cheerful despite the late hour. The patient was already on the operating table, anaesthetised. The night nursing team in theatres knew what to do. They'd brought out the surgical pack containing the large abdominal set of instruments and had got on with the rest of the preparation for exploratory surgery with quiet efficiency. It was not unusual for them to organise several emergency operations each night given how busy Mayday Hospital was.

As I started to scrub for the operation, I went over the possibilities in my head. I already had a fair suspicion of what'd happened and knew exactly what I was going to do.

From the moment that I'd been called, I was aware that there were only two possibilities to explain the catastrophic bleed.

Chris and I rapidly reopened the large transverse abdominal incision, taking out the metallic skin clips and cutting across the vicryl sutures that had been inserted to close the muscle layers and the peritoneum.

Within minutes I found what I was expecting – a large collection of blood and clots that tightly filled the space previously occupied by the cancerous kidney.

'Look, the drain's clotted off,' Chris said, referring to the silicone tube drain that I'd inserted at the end of the earlier radical nephrectomy.

'That's why there wasn't much blood in the drain bag when we checked in ITU,' he added.

A rapidly filling drain bag is an early warning sign of post-operative bleeding.

Chris and I scooped out all the accumulated blood clots and thereafter rendered the operative field dry by a combination of pressure with large abdominal swabs and deploying the sucker.

We checked the stumps of the tied-off renal artery and renal vein. The double set of violet-coloured vicryl ligatures were securely intact.

I looked at my consultant anaesthetic colleague.

'Nava, the vessels are OK. Must be the spleen.'

I remembered the difficult dissection at the top end of the kidney where most of the big tumour was. I had struggled whilst separating the upper pole of the kidney from the spleen, to which it is anatomically attached by the lienorenal ligament.

As I examined the spleen, I discovered a 2 cm tear in the capsule from which a resolute trickle of fresh blood seeped out.

I spoke again to Dr Nava.

'Yup, it's the spleen.'

'Are you going to do a splenectomy?'

'Just having a think.'

Chris asked, 'Is it worth trying to suture the tear?'

I was tempted to suture the capsular tear to stop the bleeding and preserve the spleen, which is an important organ in our body's defence system against infections.

However, suturing did not guarantee total success in staunching haemorrhage, and I didn't wish to run the risk of another major bleed.

Mr Carston had already lost a lot of blood. Although he'd been transfused with several units, we weren't replacing like with like. This is because stored blood from a blood bank is never as good in clotting ability as our own circulating blood, so there is a limit as to how much can be transfused safely.

'Look, he's already lost hell of a lot of blood,' I said. 'If he bleeds again after suture, it's going to be really dicey. Let's play safe here.'

Having weighed the pros and cons, I opted to go for the absolute safety of splenectomy. I picked up vascular clamps in preparation. The splenic artery and vein were securely tied and divided before I removed the spleen, and with it, the source of the catastrophic blood loss.

We reapplied fresh swabs, put pressure on, and waited a while before gently taking them out to see whether they were dry or blood-stained. We wanted to make 100 per cent sure that there was no further bleeding.

When we took out the swabs, I was relieved.

'Well guys, it's all dry down here,' I said aloud, articulating my own relief.

I asked Dr Navaratnarajah, 'How's he doing Nava?'

'Good... BP's come up, he's doing good,' he replied, not taking his eye off the monitors.

We inserted a fresh tube drain, and I helped Chris close up the abdomen.

*

Our patient made an uneventful recovery and went home in a week. The re-exploration didn't delay his discharge from hospital nor the period of convalescence at home. We put him on penicillin capsules to compensate for the splenectomy, as loss of the spleen increases the risk of severe infection, and wrote to his GP to vaccinate him against pneumococcus.

Over the years, I was to meet Mr Carston several times in outpatient clinics, when he came for his cancer follow-up appointments. He stayed in good health and his yearly scans confirmed that he remained free of cancer recurrence.

A few weeks after that unforgettable night, we moved out of hospital accommodation. With my first wife Baidehi, our two young children, the Labradors and five cats, we left 57 Woodcroft Road for Grove House, High Drive, Woldingham, nine miles south of Mayday Hospital, Croydon.

Our new home was within the specified radius inside which consultants who are on-call on a regular basis are contractually enjoined to reside. Over the twenty-five years that I have subsequently worked as a consultant urological surgeon in Croydon, I've been recalled to hospital on many instances and at all hours for emergencies.

On every occasion, I've had the time, during the drive from Woldingham, to endure the gnawing trepidation of all manner of imaginary horrors that I feared might lie ahead.

I didn't give much thought to 57 Woodcroft Road, apart from remembering that one eventful night in my first year as a young consultant, when I'd been able to attend a life-threatening emergency with such despatch that I hardly had time to worry.

CHAPTER 15

Abandonment – Samir's Story

The Medical College Hospitals, Calcutta - 1969

1.

I didn't know it then. I didn't know how much Samir would affect me.

It was 1969, the year of the moon landing.

I was nineteen and had just sat the First MB exam.

A month later, the results came out. That morning, after the whoops had resounded and settled around the noticeboard, I set off with my batch-mates for our familiar haunt – Coffee House on College Street. We were celebrating the completion of our anatomy and physiology courses, and the long-awaited beginning of proper clinical training.

Coffee House was Calcutta's pre-eminent *addakhana*, a place of intellectual conversation, camaraderie and dream-swapping. In the 1960s, the sun-bathed rooms with tall windows and high ceilings, on which long-bladed fans swirled, would be filled with university students crammed at square wooden tables. We would spend hours over a single cup of milky, sugar-drenched coffee – young men and women huddled together, with elbows on tables, leaning forward to debate the finer points of material dialecticism and to critique the latest recherché films of Satyajit Ray.

Most of us were also catching up with friends after the post-exam summer break, when many escaped the broiling heat of Calcutta to find refuge in misty hill stations.

'How was Darjeeling?' I asked Anjula, the slant-eyed girl sitting next to me.

'Oh, it was nice and cool. We stayed at the Windamere and managed to do some trekking. But it'll be good to get back to Medical College and start clinicals.'

'Man, I'm so looking forward to being allowed inside the wards and see patients… no more of those dreary anatomy lectures,' said Eltage, an African student living in Calcutta and studying with us on a Sudanese government scholarship.

'Well, I enjoyed dissection,' Anjula mused, referring to the afternoons spent in the anatomy demonstration hall with the pickled, desiccated corpses stacked in jack-knife position at varying stages of dismemberment. 'But it'll be so different being inside an operating theatre seeing live anatomy.'

'Yes, real action at last, the main film after the boring trailer,' butted in Dipankar, a film buff and director of our Medicos Theatre Group, running his hand through a mop of curly hair in affectation of the current matinee idol, Uttam Kumar.

*

The Medical College Hospitals had over 2,000 inpatient beds, spread over multiple departments densely packed in a sprawling dusty campus, stretching over a ten-acre rectangle in the heartland of central Calcutta. This massive inpatient capacity was easily twice the bed strength of any contemporary London teaching hospital.

The many specialist institutions that together formed the Medical College Hospitals complex were housed in individual Georgian and Victorian edifices, large enough to merit being designated 'hospital' in their own right. The Eden Hospital for Gynaecology and Midwifery, the Eye Hospital, the Hospital for Tropical Diseases, Prince of Wales Hospital for Surgery, the quaint, much smaller Ezra Hospital for medical students who themselves had fallen ill, were but some of several which made up the giant conglomerate of the Medical College Hospitals, Calcutta.

Built in 1835, during the apogee of the British Raj, this was the first medical college in Asia to impart the teaching of Western medicine.

*

A week later, we started work for the first time in the clinical settings of inpatient wards, operating theatres, accident and emergency and outpatients. The experience was a novelty. Overall, there was a feeling of exhilaration that comes with the hands-on care of patients.

Moreover, as a clinical medical student, I felt for the first time almost a real doctor. The newly purchased stethoscope, the shiny curved stainless steel leads with ivory earpieces strategically poking out of the side-pocket of a long white coat that enveloped my lanky frame, completed the ensemble. Dark framed spectacles to correct my longstanding myopia, added a certain *faux gravitas*, which I thought attracted admiring glances from the neighbourhood belles!

The year of 1969 was also when the world was in turmoil over Vietnam. In India, especially in West Bengal, the liberal left-leaning intelligentsia vociferously espoused anti-Americanism, and took out rallies with red banners in support of the plucky Vietcong.

Expressing a fine sense of irony, the Marxist government of West Bengal renamed Harrington Street, where the massive American Consulate building bristling with barbed wire was situated, to Ho Chi Minh Sarani (Sarani means thoroughfare in Bengali) in honour of the man who was the nemesis of Richard Nixon and Gerald Ford.

To my consternation, I discovered a matching turbulence within, a dark side to my heady euphoria of clinical training. It was something that I hadn't anticipated, and for which I was wholly unprepared.

I quickly found that to witness human suffering first hand was deeply unsettling. It was one thing to read up a disease in Davidson's textbook of medicine, to even look at the illustrations (in those less sensitive days, patient's faces were not redacted). To then encounter those same deformities, cancerous lumps and open tuberculous sores in a living, talking, breathing fellow human being was another matter altogether.

During my school years, I had been insulated from the general destitution that was the "Third World" India of the 1950s and 1960s. My professionally successful parents had protected me, their sole offspring, in a sterile bubble of affluence and comfort.

For the first time in my life, I came face to face with

seriously ill people. This was worsened by their abject poverty. I had not before come across suffering of this magnitude, within such touching proximity. I felt as though all the sadness of life that came from sickness and indigence, and from which I had so far been shielded, had silently accumulated and was now being dumped all over my unprepared persona.

In the very first week of ward clinical teaching, I had found it distressing to stand at the bedside of a rickety nine-year-old boy crying inconsolably, calling for his mother, while the lecturer in medicine droned on and on about Hodgkin's lymphoma, pulling down the boy's shirt collar to demonstrate the enlarged lymph nodes that stood out like marbles in his little neck.

Soon after this, confronting death for the first time, in the form of a lifeless thirteen-year-old was unimaginably disturbing. The boy had drowned in a nearby swimming pool. He'd been brought to A&E, and lay on a casualty table, lifelike in appearance, yet motionless and dead. Neighbours had rushed to inform his mother, a small pale-skinned Nepalese woman with a tiny red bindi on her forehead. I watched, frozen in my disquiet, as the distraught mother pulled in desperation her dead son's arms and legs, sobbing and beseeching, 'Baba *uth* [get up], Baba *jāāg* [open your eyes, wake *uup*].'

Each time she lifted a flail arm or leg and let go, in the hope that the limb would come to life, and that her son would sit up, it flopped down awkwardly on the trolley with a disconcerting thud.

That evening back home, my mother asked why I was quiet. I rose from the chair in my study, went over and

155

hugged her, holding her tight. I could speak no words.

Instinct told her what was troubling me.

'Bubu, it's sad, but life is harsh. You'll see many things that will distress you. Be strong and just do your very best.'

Incidents in accident & emergency, not unusual for a hospital of frenzied pace, made me question further whether I was really cut out for the tough and challenging life of a doctor.

There was the day of a horrific bus accident in the chaotic arterial road of College Street just outside Medical College. The victims had been brought straight into emergency – many were dead on arrival. I stood behind the casualty medical officers and looked in fascinated horror at the gory sight of a man's crushed face. There was very little blood visible – just a slight crimson ooze from the ears. His forehead had been pulped, and imprinted with the heavy tread of the double-decker's tyres. Yet the rest of him was untouched. I stood still, unable to tear my eyes away from the surreal incongruity stretched in front, from the unscathed neatly laced shoes, the clean socks, the charcoal-grey trousers, with sharp creases, the untarnished white shirt, and above that – the obliterated face.

Despite the daily horror-shows and the resultant churning within, I said to myself, 'No, I can't give up. I've *always* wanted to be a doctor. I've got to see this through.'

2.

My story of abandonment is set in the surgical outpatients of the Medical College Hospitals, as it was then in 1969 —

Surgical outpatients pulsates with human activity bordering on the frenetic. It is crammed to the edges with crowds of patients and relatives. There are also the many "ward boys", who in reality are grown men, employed by the hospital to carry out relatively menial tasks including disposal of ordure. In their grubby uniform of khaki sleeveless shirts and baggy shorts, this brigade of factotums bustles about with ill-placed arrogance and self-importance. They direct patients, often in peremptory manner, by sharp gestures and barked commands.

From early morning, sinuous queues form and quickly lengthen in front of the ticket office for appointments. Harassed clerks, sweating inside small cubicles, dispense numbered stubs while ignoring shouts from the rear to hasten. Medical officers cleave their way amidst the throng to consulting rooms, trying to ignore the sea of desperate, pursuing eyes.

The outpatients building is separated by a grassy enclosure from the splendid Prince of Wales Hospital, known as PWH. This is a magnificent russet-red 1830s Victorian brick building where all is calm and orderly. The non-emergency inpatient wards and operating theatres are housed in PWH. Within the edifice, polished granite floors reflect the sun's rays that pour in through tall open doorways; beds are arranged in long tidy rows in the high-ceilinged airy wards. The low hum of air-conditioning chills the operating theatres and adjacent surgeon's offices and changing rooms, a welcome refuge from the suffocating heat and humidity of Calcutta.

In contrast to the regal splendour of PWH, the nearby and separate surgical outpatients building is a squat, faded beige, one-storey quadrangular block of recent construction.

A large curved sign in bas-relief on the brickwork, impastoed in green, boldly proclaims "Outdoor Department" above the arched front entrance. There are no inpatient beds here. However ill the patient, a bed has to be sought elsewhere in a different building of Medical College.

In the interior of outpatients, there is a long central hallway that runs the entire length of the building. On either side of the hallway, a warren of gloomy rooms serve as examination chambers for those medical officers whose surgical careers have faltered and come to a halt as they had failed the MS (Master of Surgery) and FRCS exams. Medical students hurriedly pass them by, as though not wishing to be contaminated by the taint of failure. Old creaky fans, the rusty blades covered with cobwebs, circulate the humid air without conviction in these lesser habitats.

In contrast, close to the front entrance of outpatients, are two large well-lit cavernous rooms with high, rapidly whirring ceiling fans. These white-washed and well-appointed halls are reserved for the Director-Professor of Surgery and other senior consultant surgeons. Patients and relatives sit on wooden benches outside, often for hours on end, quietly waiting their turn.

Inside the hall, the Director-Professor of Surgery holds sway. Seated on a high-backed chair in front of a large rectangular desk, he resembles a High Court judge. He is surrounded by assistant surgeons and medical students. Nearby, couches covered with fabric are conveniently positioned for clinical examination and bedside teaching.

Each day, several hundreds of patients and accompanying relatives arrive from near and far, as though on pilgrimage. The Medical College, Calcutta is the referral centre for the diagnosis and treatment of conditions that are too complex for the much smaller and often poorly equipped district hospitals.

The bodily essences of this mass of humanity along with the astringent smell of disinfectant give outpatients its own distinctive miasma. It is redolent with a heady mix of apprehension bordering on fear, hope and expectation. Blended with the sweat of the tropical climate, a musk pervades. During peak hours in summer, an oppressive fug hangs in the air.

This place is nothing like the plush gleaming hospital clinics that one sees in American TV soaps. There are no automatic vending machines for drinks and refreshment. People bring their own supplies – water in plastic bottles, and for those coming from afar, small packets of dry food, in anticipation of the long hours of wait.

This is life in its bare elements, with little by way of relief.

Patients with visible disease conditions such as a disfiguring cleft lip, a protuberant thyroid goitre or crippling limb or spine deformity, form a rich lode for clinical teaching. These special patients and their relatives have even longer waits. It is not unknown for the Professor to spend the entire morning with just one case. During this prolonged teaching, once the patient has been examined and the interesting physical findings pointedly displayed, the patient himself is largely ignored while exposition on pathology, list of investigations and putative treatments are imparted as pearls of erudition to craning medical students.

Although the teaching is superb, it is uncertain whether the experience for the patient and his waiting relatives is that brilliant. This is especially so if they'd already travelled from far afield by road and rail.

The gaunt forty-year-old villager who looks in his seventies has come from a village a half day's journey by rail. As he lies down on the examination couch, his stomach hollows out like a shallow pond in a drought-stricken land.

He looks at us with bright, staring eyes.

'Babu, I'm in so much pain. And I keep bringing up blood. I'm afraid to eat anything. My wife feeds me only tiny handfuls of rice.'

The Professor of Surgery interjects.

'This is a classic case of bleeding gastric ulcer. You'll find that he is very tender when you palpate the abdomen.'

After the man has been examined by fifteen pairs of eager hands, prodding every inch of his bare stomach to elicit the exact point of tenderness, he is ready to pass out. Yet he is grateful and his only request delivered to the Professor with imploring eyes is, 'Daktar sahib, I beg you, please do my operation quickly. This pain is killing me. I cannot work, my children have no food.'

Remonstrance is unknown from this supplicant populace. Humble requests with folded palms, to be allowed to leave early and not to be detained as "teaching" cases, are curtly rejected.

The needs of the eager, white-coated medical students

to be taught and for the grandiose dark-suited consultants to teach are paramount.

*

It is against this backdrop that my own life collided with that of Samir Mahapatra.

Samir was a twelve-year-old schoolboy from a distant district of Bengal bordering Orissa. He looked tidy in short-sleeved white shirt and dark blue shorts. His hair was neatly combed and parted. There was intelligence in those deep brown eyes and warmth in his wry smile. His face reminded me of an old sepia school photo that my mother treasured. Samir had come with his father, a soft-spoken man of medium height in his late forties, wearing the traditional Bengali loose *kurta* and *dhoti*. He carried a *jhola*, the cloth shoulder-satchel, which contained the essentials for the father and son's arduous eighty-mile journey by road, rail and cycle-rickshaw. He helped and guided his son with one hand. The other clutched a rolled up umbrella that provided a modicum of protection against the blazing sun.

Samir had been suffering for weeks with severe hip pain.

'My son can hardly walk,' his father said. 'The doctors in our health centre only give us painkillers which don't work.'

He looked at his son with wistful eyes while collecting his thoughts.

'When we ask why he's in so much pain, they say, "We don't know. He needs X-rays. Take him to Calcutta, to Medical College."'

Samir was brought before the Professor of Surgery. The clinical details were read out by an assistant surgeon who stood beside the boy, with a hand on his shoulder, as though in ownership.

The Professor turned his gaze upon us, the assembled medical students. He selected me for the clinical examination.

I asked Samir to lie on the couch, and had to help him up. Gently lifting the hem of his shorts revealed a swollen left upper thigh. The skin was stretched thin and felt tense and hot. The boy grimaced even on mild touch.

There was clearly a serious abnormality – either a deep abscess or an irregularity in the underlying thigh bone. The Professor instructed me to send Samir for an X-ray.

The boy had to walk to a different building where radiology was based. An hour later, he hobbled back, leaning on his father's arm.

With deference, Samir's father handed over the single X-ray film. The Professor held up the film like a trophy. With narrowed eyes, he squinted at the X-ray negative against the sunlight of an open window.

A thin smile flitted across the Professor's face. He had made the diagnosis.

With a flourish, he snapped on the film to the clips of the portable diptych X-ray viewing box. A crepuscular shadow covered the iridescent glare of the lighted viewing box. The Professor picked up his silver Parker pen. Using it like a pointer, he traced the outlines of an expanding tumour arising from Samir's left femur, the long thigh bone. The Professor demonstrated the classical lamellated onion-peel appearance of the malignant bone tumour.

He said that along with the rapid onset of symptoms, the X-rays pointed to only one diagnosis.

He paused for a moment, glanced at Samir, and then turned his back on the boy.

The Professor looked at us and pronounced sentence.

'The diagnosis for this case is Ewing's sarcoma.'

This is a highly malignant bone cancer affecting the long bones such as the femur in the thigh and the humerus in the arm. It predominantly affects young people. Despite attempts to halt the progress of this malign bone tumour with radiotherapy or surgery, in the 1960s the disease was often fatal.

At the end of the examination, and at the conclusion of the teaching, Samir's father was handed a slip of paper with smudged writing. The instructions were to attend the hospital's radiotherapy department at a later date.

Nothing further was to be done that morning. No immediate treatment was on offer, no anodyne for the killing pain.

At the end of the morning's clinic session, the Professor and his entourage left, while we medical students prepared to go for our afternoon lectures. I stepped out to find Samir and his father sitting on the grassy verge outside. Father and son were sharing a small packet of puffed rice. Drawn and fatigued, desolation was written over their sweat-streaked faces. They both looked up at me in silent appeal. The eighty-mile trek back to their village home would again take hours. As it were, they'd risen before dawn to get to Calcutta. With the boy hardly able to walk from the excruciating pain, this was a prospect that extinguished fortitude.

An inpatient bed would be compassionate.

Obtaining an inpatient bed at short notice in Medical College was akin to winning the lottery, unless one had an immediate life-threatening condition. Given the multitude that swept up and knocked at the doors of accident & emergency with critical conditions like heart attacks, pneumonia, bowel perforation, severe trauma from accidents in the city's chaotic roads as well as knifings and stabbings, in an often strife-torn metropolis, the pressure on inpatient beds was relentless – a battle constantly fought and often lost.

The resident surgeon who was the chief admitting authority of Medical College Hospital had a strict one-line policy, which he enforced with unbending rigour. All the duty surgeons were expected to follow, without question, the mantra – "Admit only when you have to, discharge as soon as you can."

Under these austere stipulations, I knew that an entreaty to admit for a condition that was not deemed urgent, and that too a request from a lowly medical student, would have little hope of success.

Nonetheless, I found myself unable not to at least try. The boy's silent expressive eyes bravely masking his evident distress, his father's dignified appeal, 'Doctor Babu, please do something for us, Goddess Durga will bless you and your family,' impelled me to attempt finding an inpatient bed, however improbable the chances.

I went to locate the day's duty surgeon, Dr Arabinda Mukherjee. A genial roly-poly man in his late forties with unruly hair, he had recently arrived in the big city, having been promoted from a post in what we in England would disparagingly describe as "the sticks". The equally deprecatory term for this in India was *mofussil*, an expression with a colonial hangover, which denoted all things rural, and by implication, the disadvantaged areas outside metropolitan cities.

Dr Mukherjee was familiar with the woes of the village folk.

After an initial frown, he made a quiet suggestion. With a conspiratorial wink, he said, 'Gautam, why don't you try the *mattress* alternative?'

He added, 'Matron is away this week – Sister Aparna Biswas is in charge of CB Up ward today. You may just get away with it.'

On his cue, I took Samir and his father with me from the grassy verge outside outpatients, across to the John Anderson casualty block, which was the other building where surgical patients were admitted, usually for critical conditions.

The ground floor of CB or casualty block served as the accident & emergency of the Medical College Hospitals. The first floor was known as CB Up and the second floor was CB Top – both of which were surgical floors comprising inpatient wards and operating theatres.

A central winding staircase with an encased lift led off on each floor to long deep surgical wards. As you opened the collapsible iron grille and stepped out of the lift, there was a broad landing which formed an open and airy space adjoining the wards.

There were about seventy beds per ward. Each bed consisted of a sturdy iron base frame on which rested a thick whey-coloured buttoned mattress.

Amongst the many rules and regulations, it was

strict ward policy to take out the mattress for cleaning and disinfection every time a patient was discharged or died.

In times of bed shortage, when the casualty block had burst its dams, we took the unconventional, though not uncommon step of simply putting a mattress on the floor of the landing, and used it as a "bed".

I helped Samir's father take him to CB Up. There we found that, as expected, all the "normal" beds were occupied and there were no imminent discharges.

I saw Sister Biswas speaking sharply to a ward boy who had decided to take a *biri* break when he was needed to wheel a patient to the operating theatre. *Biris* were tiny (couple of puffs) yet potent cigarillos smoked by the poor as they were dirt-cheap, and in a show of comradely solidarity finely melded with inverse snobbery, also favoured by Marxist intellectuals.

She turned to me irritably, as I said, 'Sister...'

'My answer is *No!*'

'Sister, it's for this boy, he can't walk even a step. He's in so much pain.'

Sister Biswas's gaze took in Samir and his father standing a little behind me. The frown on her reddened face softened a fraction. Without an additional word, she raised a hand, which had a moment ago tensely rested on her hip, and pointed to the ward storeroom.

Barely concealing my glee at this turn of good fortune, I hauled out a clean spare mattress, plonked it on a space on the landing floor and covered it with a fresh white sheet – we had found a bed for Samir.

I was even more chuffed as the space that I had been

able to carve out was next to a wall against which Samir could prop up the solitary pillow and lean back.

The boy smiled. His father said to me, 'Babu, you've saved us.'

By then, it was early afternoon; I was late for my pathology lecture at the grand lecture theatre with its many rows of tiered seats like a Roman amphitheatre. I had missed lunch. It didn't matter; a heady euphoria had set wings to my feet.

It was evening when classes were over. The sky was darkening with louring purple clouds. It was the monsoon season, a time of heavy rain and tree-splitting thunderstorms. I was keen to get home before the squall – home, to my mother and my father, to a hot dinner, my own study, to a contented and happy household.

I thought I would drop in on Samir before going to the tram stop on College Street. He was happily ensconced in his makeshift mattress bed, sitting propped up reading a Bengali children's magazine.

He smiled when he saw me. He said, 'I'm fine here. Baba's gone back to the village. He said he'll back tomorrow morning.'

Samir held out a small pack of Britannia Thin Arrowroot biscuits that his father had purchased before leaving, a delicacy in those days.

I made my way to the tram stop in good cheer, humming the latest Bollywood hit single.

That evening, I told my mother about Samir. I related the story in minute detail. At the end, I said to her, 'Ma, I feel that I did something useful today. Something good happened in the hospital, that I did.

And Ma, you know when I saw the boy and his father smile, *I* felt happy.'

*

Next morning, before going to my lecture in the Tropical and Infectious Diseases Hospital, I thought I'd drop in at CB Up to check on Samir.

I ran up the stairs, textbooks under my arm, open white coat flailing, stethoscope draped with elegant nonchalance around my neck. I was confidently expecting and eagerly looking forward to another smile, another injection of happiness, like an addict anticipating his next hit.

I nearly bumped into one of my fellow medical students on the stairs.

'Hey Gautam, what's the hurry?'

'No time, tell you later.'

I fleet-footed to CB Up landing to see Samir.

I found the boy on his makeshift bed. But it wasn't what I'd hoped – he was crying in pain, bent over, clutching his thigh with both hands, his brow furrowed, his face darkened.

It was a shock – a cruel blow that hit me with the dual impact of the sudden and the unexpected.

A quick enquiry from the staff nurse of the morning shift revealed that, yes, he had been given his painkillers, but that he'd been like this most of the night.

I felt let down – *abandoned*.

I felt my euphoria leach away with draining rapidity. It was replaced by a corrosive resentment – an obsidian bitterness that defied reason and sought a victim – any victim.

In rough tone, I spoke to Samir. I talked down to the boy's bowed head.

'You were given medicines. I have checked with the nurses. I can't do anymore for you. You have to learn to bear.'

I turned my back on him and abruptly left for my lectures.

I endured that tiresome afternoon session on tropical diseases without a single word registering. I couldn't care less that it was the female of the anopheles mosquito that transmitted the malaria parasite.

That same evening, I went back to CB Up ward. I had in my coat pocket, a carton of Britannia Thin Arrowroot biscuits.

*

Samir did not do well. Radiotherapy was just a holding action.

More X-rays showed that his brave little chest had filled with secondaries – rounded lung shadows exemplified the textbook description of cannonball metastases that confirmed that the cancer had spread; that presaged a mother's heartbreak.

His pain became so unbearable that the surgeons had to carry out the barbaric hindquarter amputation, which is as gruesome as the name implies.

His wounds didn't heal. His body was too frail.

His immune system had abandoned him.

By now he was ill enough to deserve a proper bed – a promotion from his mattress on the floor. He was awarded bed 67 in the main ward of CB Up.

Each day I visited him.

Each evening my mother consoled me. She included Samir in the evening prayers that were offered to the family deities as she sat cross-legged on a rattan mat spread over the marble floor of the prayer room in the house. Samir's wellbeing was invoked in the holy rites that my beloved mother unfailingly observed every evening, no matter how tired she was on return home after a long day at the girl's high school where she taught senior class chemistry.

Despite my mother's succour, the black melancholy inside me refused to budge.

I was yet to acquire the detachment required for a life in the demanding practice of clinical medicine.

One morning, not long after the day I had found a bed for Samir, I went to CB Up as usual. From the entrance of the ward, I could see Bed 67 in the distance. I could see that the bed was empty.

The mattress had been taken away.

CHAPTER 16

Graham's Story – Sunt lacrimae rerum

Croydon – 1995

I first met Graham on a morning ward round a few weeks before Christmas. He lay on a hospital bed in the surgical ward, a catheter tube strapped to his leg and a blood transfusion running into his forearm. His face was pale and waxy, the sandy hair limp on his forehead.

I was the urology consultant on-call that week, and it had been busy. The house surgeon presenting the case during the ward round said, 'This sixty-four-year-old man was admitted last night from casualty with profuse haematuria [urinary bleeding]. Haemoglobin on admission was down to 6.3. Night team put in an irrigating catheter and washed out the bladder clots. They set up IV fluids and started the blood transfusion.'

Graham said that he'd first noticed a tawny-brown colour in his urine while on holiday in Cyprus.

He wasn't sure whether it was actually blood that he was seeing.

'Just thought my urine was very dark, what with being out in the sun. And I've never been one to drink a lot of water.'

That one episode had not recurred till two months

later, when he saw the undeniable red in his stream. By then he was also waking up tired.

Graham continued, 'Went to see my GP about the bleeding and also mentioned that I was feeling washed out. They tested my urine and gave me antibiotic pills. The nurse found that my weight was down 2 kilos. She said, "I'll talk to the doctor, see if you need a blood test."'

Pulling himself up awkwardly in the bed, he took a sip of water from a beaker on the side cabinet. He looked down at his catheter, 'And then last night, this happened...'

Graham's personal details in his clinical notes told us that he lived alone in Addiscombe, and that his next of kin was an elderly sister. Graham had given up smoking after a heart attack four years ago. His occupation was tersely listed as "retired bus driver".

'Started driving double-deckers from my twenties,' he said. 'Used to do the 64 route from New Addington to Thornton Heath. A lot of people got off at your hospital stop.'

Over the next two days, Graham continued to bleed, never catastrophically, but enough to require blood transfusions to top up his haemoglobin level and several catheter wash-outs to clear his bladder of blood clots.

A CT scan had been requested on admission. The SpR went down to the X-ray department to explain the urgency to the consultant radiologist and the need for prioritisation.

The CT scans showed a huge tumour arising from the upper half of Graham's right kidney, like a giant mushroom. The cancer had also spread to his lungs appearing as tell-tale cannonball secondaries, so named from their characteristic appearance on the X-ray film.

We reviewed the X-rays at our multi-disciplinary team (MDT) meeting. As the CT films were brought up on the screen in front, with the SpR reading out the clinical details, it was evident how grim the outlook was. The only glimmer of hope that we could see, lay in first reducing the volume of cancer, hence the term cyto-reductive nephrectomy, followed by chemotherapy. Oncologists and surgeons agreed that the first priority was to remove the tumour with the diseased kidney.

The radiologists showed us how hazardous that adventure was likely to be. The cancer had invaded the renal vein, and a sliver of tumour was ascending like an accusing finger up the largest vein in the abdomen, the 2 cm wide inferior vena cava that transports blood from all the lower half of the body to the heart, a nick in which, whilst operating, would lead to petrifying blood loss.

My colleagues turned to look at me – the medical oncologists with detached curiosity, the surgeons with, "Thank God, I'm not the one having to do this."

Nonetheless, there was unanimity of opinion – an operation, however risky, had to be undertaken, if nothing else to stop the bleeding. Chemotherapy could be given later for the secondaries.

I went back to the ward after the MDT meeting, to sit down with Graham. He was propped up in bed, reading the *Croydon Advertiser*. I pulled up an orange-coloured plastic chair beside his bed and drew the curtains.

'Need to talk Graham.'

I explained the need for radical surgery, what it entailed, and the risks. I had to add as gently as I could, that I couldn't guarantee that he'd survive the operation.

'Do what you must Doc,' Graham said.

'Is there anything else I can tell you about the operation?'

He shook his head.

A health care assistant half drew a curtain holding a dinner tray in one hand and withdrew at a gesture from Graham.

'Do you want a bit more time to think. Perhaps talk to your sister first,' I persisted.

'No, let's just go ahead. I'll explain to Joan when she comes this evening.'

I paged the SpR from the ward and went over the checklist in preparation for major surgery. Six units of blood were cross-matched and a bed in intensive care was reserved. We agreed the time of operation with the vascular team, whose help would be required for this difficult procedure.

I drove home that day feeling distracted. Much later, after a fidgety evening flicking through television channels, and just as I was about to turn in, I remembered what was niggling me – a recollection from twelve years ago. I was a Registrar then, in a London teaching hospital. There was an almost identical case, a man with a huge kidney tumour whom I had put on the list for nephrectomy. My boss had called me up. In frosty tones, he said that the tumour was too big, he wasn't prepared to take the risk of operating. I should never have put the patient on the list. He didn't offer an alternate plan of treatment. In those days there were no MDTs, the consultant's word was final.

*

The objective of radical nephrectomy is to remove a cancerous kidney. Whilst the central consideration is excision of the cancer in its entirety, it is also self-evident that vital organs that surround the kidney must be protected. These include liver, spleen, lung, duodenum and intestine.

Moreover, the most challenging part of the operation is to secure the pedicle or stalk of the kidney containing the renal artery and vein, both thick as a thumb, which are directly connected to the great vessels of the abdomen, the giant aorta and inferior vena cava. Hence the prudent urological surgeon recognises the *sine qua non* of assistance from vascular colleagues in difficult cases.

The renal pedicle is tucked away deep inside the abdomen, in between the substance of the kidney and the abdominal great vessels of aorta and vena cava. To get to the pedicle and tie off the renal artery and vein, the surgeon has to dissect away the surrounding vital organs and work his way deep down to an increasingly confined space – it is akin to a hazardous descent down the escarpment of a narrow ravine, right to the very bottom, there to carry out a complex task and then to come back up without dislodging a single rock or boulder from the cliff face.

Moreover, the bigger the tumour, the less accessible is the renal pedicle. Lean too strongly on the metal retractor holding the liver or spleen, and you'll tear the capsule of the organ, resulting in a furious bleed that is awkward to control. A slip of the clamp holding the renal artery will spurt a jet of hot, bright-red blood that will spatter your face mask and blind your spectacles. Avulse the renal vein, and the operative field that you have so carefully kept "dry" will rapidly sink under an alarming flood of dark, almost black venous blood.

How I wish that we "Muggles" surgeons possessed the spells of Harry Potter's Knight Bus conductor. With a suitable charm, we could command all the obstructing organs to "jump out of the way" whilst we sailed past, straight down to the renal pedicle; we could then tie off the renal blood vessels with great deliberation and remove the now bloodless kidney with its cancerous growth. After this, the liver, spleen, lungs, and bowel could simply fall back into place unharmed!

*

On the morning of Graham's operation, the theatre team led by our experienced sister-in-charge was primed of the challenge ahead. Instrument packs containing special vascular clamps and sutures were opened along with the "general" abdominal set.

We used a thoraco-abdominal incision to open the chest and abdominal cavity, in order to gain maximum exposure.

Curved retractors, their shiny metallic blades covered with large wet swabs to protect the soft and vulnerable liver, duodenum and loops of bowel were inserted and handed to the first and second assistants to hold in position to provide working space.

A first glance confirmed our worst apprehensions. The growth was so large that access to the pedicle was going to be extremely hazardous.

Moreover, to our consternation, an ample tumour

circulation was visible on the surface of the huge cancerous growth. This "tumour circulation" comprised of a snake-pit of additional blood vessels that a highly malignant tumour acquires by cannibalising the body's normal blood supply in order to feed its voracious rapidly replicating cancer cells. Repellent, both in appearance as well as in profusion, like a veritable Medusa's head, these blood vessels are also of sinister portent – always extremely thin-walled and tortuous, they tend to bleed furiously even to light touch and are notoriously difficult to control.

By tedious slow dissection and careful manipulation, working with my vascular colleague, we identified and passed a ligature around the renal artery.

The renal vein proved frustratingly much more difficult. It was a short, fat, cyan-blue stump, rising almost flush with the vena cava. The first application of a delicate Satinsky clamp slipped, resulting in spectacular blood loss. All the time, the friable vessels of the tumour circulation, despite being gently compressed with large wet swabs, continued to ooze relentlessly.

Blood was transfused early to replace the loss and to maintain blood pressure. The hiss and glug of the sucker-tube in the first assistant's hand continued unabated as we fought to keep the operating field "dry" so that visibility was maintained.

The level of blood lost in the sucker bottle rose ominously. A tear in a lumbar vein that was awkward to control led to further blood loss. The anaesthetist shouted for more blood and asked for FFP (fresh frozen plasma) which is administered to counter massive bleeding.

Circulating blood contains important plasma proteins

which are critical for the clotting process. Without these vital clotting "factors" and platelets, no amount of surgical skill can staunch blood loss from even small cuts and wounds. Donated blood stored in blood banks is relatively low in clotting factors.

FFP to an extent replaces the life-saving clotting factors and prevents a bleed that can be controlled by clamps, sutures and diathermy from becoming unstoppable because the blood simply doesn't clot.

As the evening lengthened, we were conscious that inexorably we were losing the battle. The number of blood-stained swabs multiplied at an alarming rate. The sucker bottle kept being emptied at shorter and shorter intervals. The flurry of activity at the anaesthetist's end heightened and the whispers between our anaesthetist and theatre sister became more urgent as did the phone calls to the blood bank and the haematology lab. The theatre doors banged open and shut almost continuously, with runners bringing in yet more packs of blood, FFP, and platelets.

Despite all our efforts, all the myriad ligatures and sutures, regardless of the many units of blood transfusion and FFP, Graham continued to bleed. We had entered the dreaded phase of disseminated intravascular coagulopathy (DIC) in which an abnormal and excessive activation of the clotting mechanism leads to widespread formation of numerous clots in small blood vessels. This has the dual effect of using up available clotting factors and platelets, and also shuts off the blood supply to vital organs. As the clotting factors are used up, not only is the existing bleeding worsened immeasurably but also fresh bleeding may start.

This is a most feared complication of major surgery. Attempts to clamp and suture are futile as there is no longer enough platelets and clotting factors left to seal microscopic breaches in all the tiny blood vessels. Blood replaced by transfusion simply leaks away as if through a sieve.

We carried on with the assistance of our blood bank and haematology lab to try and correct the clotting problem by replacing the coagulation factors, while at the same time packing the operative area with swabs. But it was to no avail.

Shortly before 6pm, a drop in the buzz from the anaesthetic end, followed by a muffled cough, hesitant, almost apologetic, alerted us to look up - the heart trace on the monitor was a flat line.

Graham was declared dead on the table.

A hush descended in theatre. We closed up the massive wound; in silence we tidied up and cleaned Graham's body.

Bone-tired, we took off bloodied gloves and tore off spattered gowns, caps and masks and padded to the coffee room though none of us were in the mood for refreshment. Word had spread to the other theatres. Colleagues came in and sat with us in silent support. Someone handed me a glass of cold water in a plastic cup.

Wearily, I lowered myself on a nearby chair and picked up the telephone to dial the ward and speak to the duty staff nurse.

Only the week before, I had fairly tripped down the stairs to the ward. It had been my happy task to deliver excellent news to another waiting family. That patient was a much older man. He too had undergone a difficult radical nephrectomy. His operation had been a complete success. I recalled the amusement in the accompanying medical student's eye, when the patient's wife hugged me, still in my blue scrubs, and planted a noisy wet kiss.

As staff nurse and I entered the family room, a small silver-haired lady, sprucely dressed in a beige suit, rose from her chair to greet us. She shook hands with me and bade me sit close to her.

'Are you all right? You must be very tired,' she said.

'Mrs Wright, I'm so very...' She stopped me with a gently raised palm.

Graham's elderly sister leaned forward and took my hand in both of her own. 'I want to thank you for operating on my brother. The cancer was killing him; my husband and I could see Graham fading away before our eyes.'

I continued to be silent.

'You must not be unkind to yourself. You did your best. At least, Graham had a dignified end. You gave him that.'

This was over twenty years ago – a death on the table – the one in my twenty-six-year consultant career.

*

In the immediate aftermath of such a tragedy, the entire focus of care and support is on the grieving family for their great loss, and rightly so.

For the surgeon and his team, the approach to this catastrophic event is somewhat different. Such an episode as death on the table will perhaps happen, despite all precautions and preventive measures, in the career of a surgeon with a high volume workload, especially if that work is complex surgery or cancer or major trauma.

As surgeons, we are required to be transparent about our mishaps and mistakes, learn lessons, reflect, and where necessary, tighten processes. That is what every hospital's statutory clinical governance and mortality and morbidity meetings are there for. We are then expected to move on. The desired image is that of a craggy, square-jawed Charles Bronson, not some floppy-haired weakling. We are not encouraged to fold up. Yet, if one is entirely honest, some recollections, and their effect, are impossible to entirely erase.

Some things are inescapable, even for surgeons.

Sunt lacrimae rerum – there are tears in these things – in the mind and in one's memory.

CHAPTER 17

The Silence

Calcutta 1976

It was just another Saturday afternoon at the Park Circus Tennis Club. We were playing men's doubles on Court 3.

I was in my early surgical training period at the Medical College Hospitals, Calcutta. Our training years were intense with precious little spare time for recreation. As house surgeons, we were expected to live, five to a room, in spartan doctors' messes within the hospital campus.

We spent all our waking hours scrubbed up in the operating theatres, seeing emergency admissions in the casualty block and looking after patients admitted with a variety of surgical conditions ranging from a simple groin hernia to an advanced stomach cancer.

There was no formalised, nicely typed-out on-call rota as we have in England, which in all NHS hospitals are nowadays electronically generated and circulated.

Back then, at the Medical College, Calcutta of the 1970s, we were always on-call.

Tea breaks were brief. We chose the small teashops, stacked with precariously leaning clay cups, on College Street right outside the hospital, a thoroughfare ever noisy with clanging trams and on-rolling double-decker buses.

Purchase of a cinema ticket for a late night show at

the nearest cinema hall was risky – the caper was often interrupted and usually terminated by a message on a square of white background, flashed across the middle of the celluloid screen.

The graphic interruption stunned the cinematic action and obliterated the heroine's face. The terse message, in hastily scribbled black ink, publicly exhorted the offender in Benglish (that quaint amalgam of Bengali and English) – 'House Surgeon of Prof Banerjee kindly attend CB Top ward, patient very urgent.'

In this setting, my fortnightly escapade to the tennis courts was a liberty, repaid by paring down the already grudging annual leave. It also severely depleted my store of accumulated goodwill with my immediate boss Dr Madan Chowdhury (Madanda), our avuncular, balding, much-loved resident surgeon, who tolerated our occasional jaunts with mock ticking-off.

'Gautam, where were you last Saturday? We had an interesting case of intestinal obstruction from roundworm infestation. I was looking for you.'

'Madanda, it was my tennis afternoon. You'd said "yes" when I asked you two weeks ago,' I protested weakly.

'Hmm… well Gautam, tennis and training… hmm, not a good combination,' Dr Chowdhury looked out of his postage stamp office window. He shook his head with that classical Indian wobble of equivocation – an equal mixture of reproval and indulgence.

Playing tennis was also a throwback to the undoubted advantage of my relatively privileged background – as the sole offspring of parents, both of whom were professionally successful. This was especially so in a city that did not reek of affluence and at a time when few in India could claim to be rich or even comfortably off.

Our giant metropolis of Calcutta was densely populated. Space was as cherished as gold dust. Greenfield and brownfield sites alike constantly fought a losing battle of attrition against a protean acquisitive and growing populace. This had been the script from my boyhood days long years ago.

The playing fields of Calcutta were richly prized and keenly guarded. In this seething city of fifteen million, greenery was forever fighting a recurring battle of survival.

This conflict was reflected in the lives of the vast population of indigent subalterns who lived cheek-by-jowl mired in the squalor of rickety huts and hutments. These ubiquitous *bustees* or slums housed hundreds and thousands of poor souls scratching out a meagre existence. They eked out a subsistence living in close proximity to the often opulent brick and concrete mansions of the well-heeled professionals and the inherited rich. This affluent *corps d'élite* also included the nouveau riche, whose often dubious business practices and resultant pelf were extravagantly displayed in the swagger of their swanky abodes.

It was for these patrician classes that the elite sports of tennis and badminton were reserved. Given the usually clement weather and bountiful sunshine, outdoor grass courts outnumbered covered indoor sports centres.

These lush grass courts were lovingly and proprietorially watered and tended by *maalis* (specialist gardeners). Most tennis clubs were managed with a firm hand by an imposing club chairman. Invariably, this would be a retired army officer, an impressively be-whiskered gentleman in natty outfit of navy blazer, even at the height of summer, and de rigueur regimental tie.

These then were the playing fields of the Calcutta elite. It was here that the scions of the ruling tribe exercised their young bodies and honed their reflexes in the spirit of *mens sana in corpore sano* (a healthy mind in a healthy body). It was these same youngsters who in the evenings, went off to language classes run by the Max Muller Institute of the German Consulate and the Alliance Française, intellectual first cousins and rivals of the British Council, competing for cerebral and cultural space in the minds and hearts of the modern Bengali young and impressionable.

Evening conversations at the Royal Cooch Behar Lounge of the Calcutta Club between paterfamilias, who themselves were covenanted officers in British mercantile firms like Andrew Yule and Mackinnon & Mackenzie, would often take a familiar route.

'Mr Bose, how's your boy Indrajit doing? Isn't he due for his Senior Cambridge exams this year?'

'Yes, we're making sure he works hard at it.'

'Which university is he expecting to go to?'

'Well, we're hopeful that his grades would be good enough for Oxford next term.'

Mr Bose rang the bell on the coffee table twice in quick succession, as though anticipating a dilatory response from the club's shuffling, elderly "bearers" in faded white uniforms with red sashes.

As he waited for his Scotch and soda with just one cube of ice and a Bloody Mary for his fellow club member, Mr Bose reflected, 'We think competence in German will strengthen his application. It was the new Rector at St Xavier's, Father Desbruslais's suggestion, given the competition the lads face these days.'

Tennis was the bodily equivalent of French and German. During my schooldays at the city's premier boys' high school of St Xavier's and my university years as a medical student in the renowned Medical College Hospitals, Calcutta, my father paid the not insubstantial fees for my annual membership of the Park Circus Tennis Club.

The club itself was located near the plush end of Calcutta, a stone's throw from brassy Park Street and exclusive Chowringhee, yet not far from a dingy slum which was the recruitment hub for the ball-boys.

Now, these were not the firm-limbed, bright-eyed, adolescent schoolboys and girls with glowing faces that you are familiar with at Wimbledon, Roland Garros and Flushing Meadows.

These were scrawny, malnourished, grimy eight- to twelve-year-olds, some even as young as six or seven.

Apart from the odd religious *madrassa* or NGO-run tin-roofed basic primary school, these boys had never seen the inside of a proper educational establishment. Yet their inquisitive minds were rapier sharp, as revealed in their conversation and discourse.

These kids had been sent out by their dirt-poor parents to gather and bring home the crumbs that would attempt to supplement the woefully inadequate family income. The fathers were usually manual labourers with backbreaking, unhealthy construction jobs, while the mothers worked long hours as domestic helps or *ayahs* to the memsahibs of the neighbouring mansions.

Our particular pack of picaresque urchins were no different in background or behaviour. They good-naturedly chased after stray tennis balls and threw them back with accuracy.

They did not cavil at their day-long Sisyphean task.

At the end of the afternoon, when the setting sun spread a mellow orange glow over the opaque and pollution-ridden city sky, when the sweat had cooled and pulses slowed, this eager platoon would jostle and badger for *baksheesh*, refusing to be fobbed off with mere coins.

For some reason, this sharp-eyed, jolly pack had singled me out amongst my peers, for their attention and favour. Apart from the discussion about *baksheesh*, they displayed an engaging curiosity about me, my family and my life.

After the last set had been won and lost, when the mundane business transactions over *baksheesh* were over, the serious conversations would begin.

'What *jaat* [caste] are you?' asked nine-year-old Arif.

Before I could answer, another of the waifs, Rahim, an older, taller boy, had spotted the edge of my *taabiz*, the copper amulet tied with consecrated red thread to my upper arm.

Elated with the joy of discovery, he whooped, 'Look! Look at his *taabiz*! He must be Hindu.'

To prove his point, Rahim pulled up the short sleeve of my tennis shirt with a quick movement of a sun-darkened hot hand, scratchy with grime, to fully display the talisman on my arm, that had been blessed by the priest at the Kali temple, and which my mother had herself fastened, to ward off evil.

'Where's your sacred thread?' another asked.

I had the feeling that my answer would disappoint.

'I don't have one,' I said, as though confessing a major shortcoming like leprosy.

'Oh!! He's not Brahmin then,' said yet another in a tone that indicated, with no room for uncertainty, that I had somehow failed them – by not being upper rank *kulin* Brahmin, right at the apex of the Hindu caste hierarchy – like a Banerjee, Mukherjee or Chatterjee, though the boys themselves were all Sunni Muslim, a faith that frowns upon distinction amongst men based on caste.

The deliberations would then move on to what I had been served for dinner the night before. This would be compared, in an almost detached manner, with their own modest fares. There was not a jot of envy, no prickly line of malice. I would be proudly informed of how many *sleeces* (slices) of roti their impoverished mothers had put in front of them.

One of these Oliver Twists was a particularly alert eight-year-old with the endearing name of Feku.

Now that name has a negative connotation in the North Indian lexicon. Quite simply it means reject, a discard with all the implied cruelty of such a moniker.

It is probable that his parents resented the unexpected extra mouth to feed, that perchance he'd arrived at a time of adversity, of illness, perhaps disastrous loss of employment.

Feku, however, lived a life of insouciance. No care furrowed his little brow. The size of the day's end *baksheesh* appeared not to bother him unduly. Not for him any petulance or rancour. Ever on the tip of his tongue was ready banter and repartee in his rough Hindustani, especially when urged on at his task of tennis ball collection. His goodwill and happy nature were infectious. The little chap was a flitting ray of sunshine for all around him.

At the other end of the club's social spectrum were of course, the dapper young blades, myself included, kitted out in crisp Persil white sports shirts and shorts with matching designer trainers, who owned and wielded expensive tennis racquets.

We were of a class that unquestioningly took our privileged station in life as wholly natural. We possessed an unshakeable sense of entitlement.

Nevertheless, though overtly hierarchical, an easy and congenial relationship existed between haves and have-nots. The overall atmosphere in the club was friendly and convivial as would be natural to any sporting environment

*

That sunny Saturday afternoon, it was business as usual. All eight grass courts were in use. The club chairman Mr Ghoshal went round with the head *maali* pointing out arid patches that required extra attention. The iced lemonade chilled in dewed glass jugs covered with fabric doilies.

It was in this genteel setting that the incident occurred.

I was on court 3, the one overlooked by the newest garishly painted high-rise. One of my opponents, in the opposing men's doubles team, was the youngest scion of an old aristocratic family from the northern *zamindari* side of the city's cultural and social divide.

This is the section of Calcutta where amongst the prosperous elite, inherited wealth prevails, and sometimes brings with it in equal measure the enervating and unappealing traits of snobbery and hubris.

In outward appearance though, this young man was no different to the rest of us.

That afternoon he let the side down. He behaved abominably. Perhaps it was the worry of inadequate preparation for final college exams, perhaps his father had sternly remonstrated for overspending his generous allowance, or maybe his current girlfriend's affections had cooled.

Whatever it was, it resulted in an act that was shameful and puerile, and so out of character of the ethos of our club.

After a cross-court shot that landed just outside the chalk resulting in the loss of a tightly fought set, Feku had returned the ball. Perhaps it was not quick enough, perhaps it had not been thrown back straight at the prince's feet.

The young tennis player from North Calcutta did the unthinkable.

'Shit!' he yelled, and smashed the tennis ball straight back at Feku.

Whatever the intended aim, the ball ricocheted off the boy's face like a rifle shot.

Play stopped in horror. I dropped my racquet and ran to Feku. Still standing brave-faced, an angry red weal rapidly spread over the left side of his little face. The eye was closed. Tears silently coursed down the cheeks of the forlorn small boy.

By consensus, it was agreed that Feku needed to be

taken straightaway to an emergency unit to have the injured eye checked out. Given my medical background and the fact that my car was parked nearby, my offer to do the needful was readily accepted by the chairman.

I took Feku in my blue Morris Minor, a generous gift from my indulgent father. A whole troupe of Feku's comrades followed and piled in.

In those carefree days, seat belts were unheard of, and the limit on the number of passengers was arbitrary - you got in as many as you could.

I had a scrum of excitable boys filling every nook and cranny of the car interior. Some were standing, some sitting, and some others sitting on older boy's laps. One of them was tightly wedged next to me on the driving seat, the close-cropped head a bristly rub against my left elbow every time I changed gear.

Outside the car, in the dense peak-hour traffic of Lower Circular Road, the road noise was a sledge-hammer through the open windows of the Morris Minor. There was the relentless blare of bus and car horns from that uniquely mindless Indian habit of leaning on the vehicle horn even whilst at a standstill. Adding to the tumult, the raucous cries and shouts of perspiring cart pullers and the metallic clang of tramcar bells cleaved the humid evening air.

Inside the Morris Minor, as they were piling in, there had been a hyper-excitable babble of clamour and chatter, as a dozen small boys jostled and elbowed for space, quite forgetful of why they were there in the first place.

And then suddenly, after we had set off and gone but a few yards, an all-encompassing silence descended

– a preternatural stillness that initially flummoxed and unnerved me, a silence that obliterated all other senses, a hush that overpowered the atonal bedlam of the road outside.

And then it came to me – these boys born in poverty and raised in indigence had never been inside a car before. No one had ever taken them for a journey in a motorcar. This was an experience that was entirely novel, a treat they had never before enjoyed.

Dear God, I could have wept. I felt deeply humbled to have witnessed and to have been a minor player in the sublime purity of that moment.

And then as suddenly as it had appeared, the ephemeral moment was gone.

Gone forever in the ether of eternity to join that limitless swirl of human experiences – of joy and sorrow, ying and yang, that together make up the human condition.

This is what the Japanese define as *utsoroi* – transience. Just as the cherry blossom tree flowers in splendour and then falls and perishes in a short week, so do all good things, and life itself – cloaked as they are in impermanence, and therefore all the more precious, to be recognised and appreciated, loved and cherished, while it is there.

The boys resumed their excited chatter.

In a short while, we drew up at the Central Avenue entrance of the sprawling Medical College Hospitals complex. Just inside Gate no. 5, as we turned in past a thicket of pedestrians, was the red-brick Eye Hospital and affiliated Institute of Ophthalmology.

I herded our motley flock into the emergency section, where we sat in companionable proximity in the waiting area, on benches whose brown rexine covers were cloven with many rents.

The overhead strip lighting picked out a curious tableau of a young man kitted out in immaculate sporting apparel of snow-white T-shirt and shorts with a small boy leaning on his arm surrounded by other small boys also wearing shorts and sleeveless shirts but of more modest provenance.

Our wait was not for long. The duty ophthalmologist was Dr Mitra, a genial middle-aged man with a luxuriant peppery moustache. He recognised me and beckoned us in to the examination room.

With great care, Dr Mitra swabbed Feku's left eye with cool saline-soaked cotton wool balls. He leaned over, bringing the ophthalmoscope close to Feku's face. The skirring sound of the instrument's focus lever was heightened in the stillness of the room.

After a few minutes, Dr Mitra straightened up and smiled.

'Good, there's no corneal abrasion and no intra-ocular haemorrhage.'

He looked to me and added, 'Just make sure that he puts in some eye drops for the next few days.'

After a slight pause, he gently said, 'Wait.'

Dr Mitra turned around to open a large upright steel cabinet with peeling slate-grey paint. He fished out a small bottle capped with a dropper lid. It was a physician's sample from his personal stock given by a pharmaceutical rep.

Feku came out with us clutching the precious eye drops in his fist like a trophy.

He was back at the tennis courts the next morning.

CHAPTER 18

A Multi-Millionaire in Harley Street
–

London – 2015

My good friend Richard Pinkerton told me this story over a gin and tonic at the member's bar of the Royal Society of Medicine. We had both been to the section of urology meeting that evening and were killing time before catching our respective trains home from Victoria Station.

A 6 ft 4 bear of a man with a mop of dark brown hair, imbued with a calm and thoughtful manner, Richard was an expert in andrology, the branch of urology that specialises in men's sexual disorders.

Richard held an academic senior lecturer post at a London teaching hospital, where he was also an NHS consultant.

The international reputation that he deservedly enjoyed, from his research into xenon gas washout to measure blood flow in the penis, and the many scientific papers which were published in prestigious medical journals, did no harm to a burgeoning private practice that knocked on the polished doors of his well-appointed rooms in Devonshire Place, right next to the London Clinic.

Richard's story that evening started off initially with a certain Hasan El-Jabbar, an Emirati businessman.

*

Hasan was in his mid-forties. A squat, bald man, his personality matched the girth of his midriff. As if to compensate for the smooth dome of his head, he sported a bristly moustache, above which tufts of coarse nostril hair poked out.

'I'm very happy to meet you doktore, I feel sure you help me,' was his opening remark after he'd been ushered in with his wife into the oak-panelled consulting room.

On being invited to sit down, Hasan El-Jabbar leaned forward to spread podgy hands on Richard's walnut table. He turned to his wife beside him, and said, 'Roya, show doktore my papers.'

Richard looked across towards a strikingly attractive, tall and slim young woman, whose exceptional beauty could not be concealed by the hijab that immured her hair except for an escaped silken strand. The headscarf was grape-coloured, not black, more an adornment than a statement. Nor was her niqab a deterring face mask, instead it was a diaphanous muslin mouth-veil that accentuated rather than obscured the sensuous fullness of her lips.

Moreover, the hijab and niqab had the effect of emphasising the most arresting feature of Roya El-Jabbar's face – her light topaz eyes that even in the muted light of a late September afternoon held as much sparkle as a morning dew-drop in spring.

With a low, richly modulated voice, she said, 'Excuse me a moment, Mr Pinkerton.' Her 't's were softly enunciated, almost a lisp from the back of her upper teeth.

195

Richard observed her with ingrained unobtrusiveness, as she swung a taupe-grey Birkin shoulder bag on to her lap.

His glance at the flawless milk-white face took in the flash of the discreet diamond nose stud; yet he was drawn again to those alluring long-lashed, kohl-rimmed eyes.

Roya El-Jabbar unfastened the clasp of the veau leather bag and took out a thick folio, neatly bound with blue ribbon.

'Here are my husband's medical reports from Dubai.' She met and held Richard's gaze with a smile, as she handed him the folder with a fleeting touch of warm fingertips.

The paperwork from Dubai stated that Hasan had complained of weak erections and some pain while ejaculating. The local urologist had been thorough, both in his physical examination, as well as with the investigative tests.

Nothing untoward had been identified apart from a weight issue and a touch of high blood pressure. The fasting blood sugar level was borderline.

The Dubai urologist had correctly advised dietary restraint and regular exercise. Viagra had been prescribed to enhance sexual performance.

Mr El-Jabbar however, impatient for instantaneous results, had chosen to seek an immediate second opinion at Harley Street.

'I'm not OK, not good. I want top advice,' he said, beaming as though to ingratiate himself with his specialist. 'I come to Harley Street for best treatment.' He smoothed his moustache with stubby fingers as if to add emphasis.

'I do international business, make many many millions of dollars,' he declared proudly, his gesticulating hands carving large domains out of the air, and pronouncing millions as "mee – leons". Hasan cleared his throat loudly. 'I have business in real estate, transport, solar technology, my business take me everywhere. For my health, I want best medicine.'

Further warming to the subject of his health, he continued, 'My wife,' he nodded towards Roya. 'She top journalist in Dubai, she check for me and say you best doktore in Harley Street for my problem.'

Acknowledging the encomium with a wry polite smile, Richard gestured to his patient with his open palm, inviting him to go through to the adjoining examination room.

Before going across, Hasan snapped off his Rolex Yachtmaster, and emptied out his pockets – placing a Vertu smartphone and monogrammed Louis Vuitton wallet along with the gold wristwatch on Richard's consulting room table.

In the examination cubicle, away from his wife, Hasan unbuttoned his cream silk shirt releasing a whiff of stale armpits not quite neutralised by the heavy overlay of expensive cologne. He had to pull in his stomach in order to undo the belt of his trousers before lying down on the couch.

In confidential undertone, he told Richard, 'Last month, I come here Lundun for business trip. I come alone,' he added with a wink as if to seal a conspiracy.

In this, Hasan was not unlike many other men, with worries or actual problems arising from a later regretted clandestine assignation, confessing to their doctor what they would keep from their priest.

As Richard squeezed a blob of KY jelly on the tip of his gloved forefinger in preparation for carrying out a prostate examination, Hasan El-Jabbar displayed no apprehension. His face crinkled into an amused look. Expansively, he said, 'I no allow even my wife touch me there,' chuckling at his own witticism.

At the conclusion of the clinical examination, Richard escorted Hasan back to the main consulting chamber to rejoin Roya, who had been sitting patiently, flicking through a week-old copy of the *Tatler* that she had earlier picked up from a pile of magazines in the downstairs reception area.

Adept at handling sensitive medical conditions of a sexual nature, adroit at dealing with the often psyched-up person around the condition, and possessing a flair in discerning exactly what was expected by the demanding medical tourist, Richard concluded the consultation by taking a reassuring stance whilst organising further tests including an MRI scan.

In addition, given Mr El-Jabbar's implied confession of a peccadillo during his earlier solo visit to London, a blood screen to check for sexually transmitted diseases (STD) was ordered.

Hasan was also discreetly asked to provide a semen sample for lab analysis, to check if he had a prostate infection.

Throughout the consultation and whilst her husband was being examined, Roya El-Jabbar had sat with dignified composure. Not once had she interrupted while Hasan spoke, nor had she displayed indifference to her husband's concerns. She had diligently written down on a slim black leather notepad Richard's instructions, as well the dates for tests and follow-up consultation.

Despite himself, Richard had not been able to suppress the occasional sidelong glance to admire her serene presence. He could not help but notice the graceful ivory hand with long tapering fingers that were immaculately manicured, the fingernails attractively coloured with a matte polish of orchid pink.

A few days later, when the packet of test results dropped on Richard's desk, he saw that the MRI was normal and the STD screen was clear.

The semen analysis result was not through as yet.

*

For the next two days, Richard had to be away from his busy practice in London. He would be in Edinburgh, examining for the oral component of the Final Fellowship of the Royal College of Surgeons.

Before leaving London, Richard left instructions with Gillian, his briskly efficient secretary of many years, to telephone him with any queries about his patients or abnormal lab results.

Then, indulging as he did at every opportunity a boyhood love for locomotive journeys, Richard boarded the overnight train to Edinburgh from Euston. The last week had been particularly tiring – he'd been on-call most nights. Richard was looking forward to this break from routine. As soon as he was inside his coupé in a first-class coach of the Caledonian Sleeper, he kicked off his shoes and sank into the luxury of the crisp white sheets and deep bedding with a long pent-up sigh.

In Edinburgh, he could have stayed at any of the plush

hotels on Princes Street. Instead he hailed a cab at Waverley station and gave the Dumfries born-and-accented Pakistani taxi driver the address of the Newington Guest House.

He was welcomed with a hug and, 'Ooh, lovely to see you again Richard. How're Lynne and the children?'

He'd known the landlady Jeanne from his junior doctor days when he'd come up to Edinburgh for training courses and to take his own exams.

They were both young then. Richard was an apprentice surgeon, whilst twenty-two-year-old auburn headed, wasp-waisted Jeanne ran her widowed mother's guest house with energy and flair. Her gift of recollection - names, events, anniversaries, foibles - the child with peanut allergy, the elderly lady who couldn't sleep on goose down pillows ensured a loyal return clientele.

Jeanne would always make sure that the lanky Sassenach had the quietest room in the B&B. She would wait patiently after clearing away the breakfast tables to cook him something hot the mornings he woke late after a night of studying.

Even after Richard had advanced to senior consultant in the NHS, he'd never considered staying anywhere else on his many visits to the city.

Early on his first morning in Edinburgh, Gillian called his mobile.

'The lab's just faxed through an abnormal result. The patient's Mr El-Jabbar.'

Gillian proceeded to read out Hasan's semen analysis report.

Without interrupting, Richard heard in full detail the startling test result.

He hung up, thought for a moment, and then pressed the speed-dial key on his Blackberry for the pathology laboratory in Wimpole Street. He asked to be put through to the duty lab scientific officer.

'Hi Rob, bit surprised with the result of Mr Hasan El-Jabbar's semen sample.'

'Mr Pinkerton, I've looked at the slides myself – the report is absolutely accurate. I've also double-checked the date of the sample as well as the patient's personal details.'

'Hmm, OK Rob, thanks. Guess I'll just have to do a Madeleine Albright with this one and "tell it like it is".'

*

For the two days that he was in Edinburgh, Richard put aside all thoughts of Hasan El-Jabbar and his unusual semen result and focused on the FRCS examinations at the Royal College.

Richard enjoyed the twenty-minute walk, at a slight skyward incline, starting from the guest house on Newington Road, up the length of South Clerk Street to Nicolson Square, home of the Royal College of Surgeons.

As always, there was the joy of recognition – to see Surgeon's Hall from a distance… to observe the imposing Corinthian columns rising to support the inscripted architrave, and as he got closer, to admire the frieze and surbaisse pediment, marvelling each time at the architectural magnificence of William Henry Playfair's neo-classical Edinburgh landmark.

He found it stimulating to be a Royal College examiner – not just the sheer power, the one-sided testing of knowledge, of deciding the fate of the nerve-wracked candidates, but equally the interaction with fresh young minds from all over the United Kingdom and beyond. He also found that, although a senior surgeon, he too learned something new each time.

The day after his return to London, Hasan and Roya El-Jabbar were scheduled to come back to Devonshire Place to be given the test results.

Richard pondered how he was going to break the news to the couple that Hasan's semen sample had showed an unsuspected abnormality.

He had *azoospermia* – complete absence of sperms in the seminal fluid.

The man was infertile.

This was an entirely unexpected finding. It would come as an unwelcome surprise to Hasan and his wife, given that they'd come to London for a fairly commonplace men's complaint and not specifically to seek fertility advice.

*

As on their first visit, Hasan preceded his wife into the consulting room.

An ebullient, 'Hello doktore' and a friendly, 'Good evening Mr Pinkerton,' were offered across the desk.

Following a time-tested technique of communication in breaking bad news, Richard started by putting his clients at ease with the good bits of the consultation, giving out investigation results that were favourable.

'I'm pleased to say that the prostate MRI and all the blood tests were completely normal.'

'Good, good, doktore. I worry about prostate cancer. Look, big report in your newspaper today.' He thrust the *Daily Mail* at Richard quarter-folded like a Shakespearean quarto, to reveal the medical column.

Richard cleared his throat and continued, 'Your semen test happily showed no signs of infection at all.'

He paused, and tentatively pressed on, 'The sperm count—'

'Yes, yes, many many mee-leons, eh doktore?' Hasan interjected with a belly laugh.

At this point, Richard slowed down, but he didn't have to stonewall as the ebullient Hasan was unstoppable in his high-octane outpouring.

Whipping out his cellphone, he thrust it, lighted screen face-up, in front of Richard. 'Look, look, my boys, Sohail and Salim, this one twelve,' he jabbed at a face on the screensaver. 'This one ten, both strong... like their father, both play rugby, play football.'

Stunned, Richard stared at the image on the iPhone – he looked at the faces of two young boys, grinning with the unalloyed happiness that is possible only when one is that young.

He tore his gaze away, and as he looked up, unsure of what to say next, his peripheral vision was pierced by a look of such intensity that for a moment he lost concentration. He was acutely conscious of two beseeching eyes boring into him.

Those smoky eyes held such fervent appeal that Richard almost turned to her to confirm the speechless entreaty.

That day Richard Pinkerton took a decision, a lonely

one, for he would be on his own if there were to be comebacks. The facial muscles of his mouth, those delicate fascicles of orbicularis oris, relaxed into a reassuring smile.

Without missing a beat, without breaking eye contact with Hasan, squaring his shoulders and drawing himself up with the full gravitas of a famous Harley Street consultant, he said, 'Yes Mr El-Jabbar, as you yourself asserted the other day, you are indeed... a multi-millionaire!'

Richard thought he heard a soft sigh, gentle as the rustle of a falling leaf.

CHAPTER 19

"The Opium of the Masses" and a Man of Character

Surrey, 2014 and the Medical College Hospitals, Calcutta, 1969

It was quiz night at the Fox and Hounds, our local pub in Warlingham. The quizmaster, a young man with pointy ears and a blotchy complexion, thought that he had us stumped when, moving on from great strikers of the English Premier League 1979–89, he solemnly declared, 'The next segment is on European politics in the nineteenth century.'

Plunging on despite the audible groans and hoots from the younger tables, he looked expectantly at the senior section and asked, 'Who wrote - "Religion is the opium of the masses"?'

Our interrogator looked bemused when he was shot back with an instantaneous correct reply.

Driving home later that night, my wife Susan, herself a senior nursing sister, asked without taking her eyes off the headlights that pierced the pitch-black of Woldingham village's darkened country lanes, 'Isn't it equally true, that although opium is an addictive substance, it is also a strong painkiller?'

Before I could ask where she was going with this

rhetorical question, Susan added, 'Karl Marx would've known that opium was widely used for pain. God knows how many Victorian women took laudanum for menstrual cramps...' She paused while slowing down at a sharp turn past the North Downs golf club. '... Could it be that Marx, perhaps even unintentionally, was acknowledging that religion was of some help for the poor in those days?'

I struggled with that question. A few days later, as these things often happen, an anecdote came to my rescue – a narrative that swept me back to a time when I was a young medical student and life bristled with promises. In order to re-examine Marx's polemic, I had to rewind the clock till the hands stopped at a point that settled on the Calcutta of 1969. My recollections brought to life a singular period of my existence and put flesh on a man of character.

*

At the Medical College, Calcutta of the late 1960s, our surgical training was shaped and sharpened by many eminent surgical teachers. One of these master-surgeons was Dr Syed Abdul Momin, a tall, light-skinned man in his mid-forties with straight hair brushed back from the forehead. His bearing was upright though he carried a few extra pounds, mostly around the middle, reflecting his wife's culinary skills. Of jocular disposition, Dr Momin was known to all and sundry as Mominda (the suffix *da* to a Calcutta name denotes a respected older male with whom one enjoys a relationship of warmth and closeness, like an older brother).

This consultant was especially popular with the medical students for a gallimaufry of qualities – a conscientious surgeon, he possessed a delicate and safe pair of hands, as observers in the operating theatre would attest, and patients benefit from; he was an inspiring teacher who could render the most arid subject, even the life-cycle of the liver fluke, interesting with his style and delivery. Best of all, he was easy-going and approachable with not the slightest tinge of hauteur that was sadly so common amongst many surgeons possessed of a lofty and all too often misplaced sense of self-importance.

Mominda was the quintessential older brother to whom one could always turn for guidance. It was my good fortune to have known him as one of my mentors from medical student days to house surgeon years.

Dr Momin was born a Muslim who wore his faith lightly, never projecting his religious conviction in an overt manner. No beard concealed his jawline, no *taqiyah* skullcap covered his head; he was never known to interrupt work to say *namaaz* prayers. He was wholly comfortable with the societal reality of India where the overwhelming majority of his students, colleagues and patients were Hindus.

Amongst the norms of our medical college in those untroubled days was the tradition of clinical teachers inviting medical students, who were in their teaching "firm", for a meal at home on completion of the three-month period when the students were "attached" to the consultant, following him on ward rounds like ducklings in a row, and accompanying him to the operating theatre.

In keeping with this treasured convention, one November evening in 1969, a few weeks after the *Durga*

Puja festivities, the Hindu Bengali equivalent of Christmas, six of us medical students were invited to Mominda's home for dinner.

Dr Momin lived with his wife in Mullick Bazar where bearded men in flowing sherwani (similar to a long frock coat) and loose pajamas accompanied their womenfolk encased in black burqa and veil, where the bargains struck inside the small shops that crowded the narrow dimly-lit alleys were conducted in Urdu (the language of Indian Muslims), and where the mouth-watering smell of freshly grilled kebabs on long skewers and rotis baking in red hot tandoors drew you into the plentiful roadside eateries. This was where the puissance and reach of the muezzin's call to prayer unmistakably proclaimed that you were in the Muslim quarter of Calcutta.

Here in Mullick Bazar, the expectation of repast in a Muslim household was that of Mughlai cuisine, prepared from exotic recipes created and handed down the generations, right from the times of the great Mughal emperors of India.

Our evening at Dr Momin's place promised to be an ambrosial experience, so different from the uninspiring everyday fare of runny daal, coarse rice and bland vegetables that was dished out in our student's hostel with matching indifference; where only one day a week, was meat served – a watery mutton stew, that too mostly gristle, bone and fat.

Classmates who had previously been to Mominda's house for their end-of-firm repast reported back in effusive terms of the toothsome home cooking of Mominda's wife, *Boudi* (the Calcutta Bengali term for an older brother's wife).

I myself was secretly looking forward to beef biryani. In India, beef in any shape or form was strictly forbidden in Hindu households that made up an overwhelming 85 per cent of India's population. The reverence towards the sacred cow meant that all practising as well as "by name only" Hindus abjured cow meat. Even the smell of beef would taint a Hindu home and pollute a Hindu housewife's hearth.

Nonetheless, many of us though born to the Hindu faith, yet educated within a "Western" curriculum in Christian missionary schools, coupled with the innate derision of rebellious youth towards rules and taboos, were always eager to partake of that which was prohibited at home and the student's hostel.

On that autumnal evening of our invitation, when Calcutta was at last enjoying the relief of cool draughts after eight relentless months of tropical heat and humidity, Boudi excelled herself. As soon as we had rung the rusty entry bell and pushed open the front door to Mominda's two-room apartment, a tantalising aroma of cloves and cinnamon, roasted chilli, mustard seed and cumin instantaneously livened our olfactory receptors and gave notice to our dormant taste buds.

We exchanged *namaste* greetings with Mominda and Boudi, took off our shoes, washed our hands with a bar of Lifebuoy soap at the single cold water tap in the basin, and sat down under the neon lighting of the small dining room, which connected to the kitchen through an archway.

In front of us was laid out a sumptuous banquet – platters of tandoori chicken, fiery red with their dusting of paprika, jostled with tureens of succulent lamb biryani, and steaming basmati rice, topped with whole almonds and raisins. Salvers piled with pan-fried pomfret fish, and serving dishes filled with curried eggs, and prawns slow-cooked in coconut-milk fought for space with oval plates stacked with fingertip-burning buttered roti. Several vegetable side dishes of okra, brinjal and aloo jeera, sprinkled with sprigs of coriander, squeezed in.

This was the not uncommon exemplification of the "guest is god" philosophy of an Indian housewife. In a further act of consideration, respectful of her Hindu guests' religious sensitivities, Boudi had not prepared beef.

In the midst of this banquet, fidgety with my disappointment of not finding the one thing that I craved that evening, churlish despite all the other delicacies, and knowing that in a Muslim household, a beef dish must exist somewhere, secreted away safely from the "beefless" feast, I got up from my chair with the nonchalance that only an irrepressible nineteen-year-old, mindless of consequence, is capable of, and headed straight for the kitchen through the open archway. I opened the fridge door, and just as a circling shark senses a drop of blood in the ocean, discovered, tucked away behind several food packets, utensils and cartons, and right at the back of the lowest cabinet, the porcelain container of beef biryani.

Mominda, alerted by his wife, rushed in.

'Gautam, what are you doing? That's *beef*.'

'Exactly Mominda, and before you tell me off, please remember that Derozio was my distant great-uncle.'

Every Calcuttan was instantly familiar with the name Henry Vivian Louis Derozio, the iconic nineteenth-century

Anglo-Indian poet, firebrand and freethinker, who in an eventful life cruelly cut short at twenty-two by cholera, had revolutionised the minds and spirit of Bengali youth by repudiating religious orthodoxy and obscurantism.

Invoking Derozio to bolster any intellectual argument in Calcutta was the equivalent of firing a Taser gun to the opposing debater, such was the reverence with which the apostle of Indian modernity was held.

Mominda was temporarily nonplussed.

He knew that Derozio's name was synonymous with the rejection of the theological straitjacket of strict vegetarianism in favour of meat consumption including the "untouchable" beef.

In those bygone days of imperial British rule, Derozio had encouraged his skinny Bengali college students to eat meat, to strengthen their sinews and muscles, for the fight to win freedom from colonialism.

Summoning Derozio, still a messiah in the twentieth century, with his powerful and enduring message of *reason* that had helped usher in India's age of enlightenment, was a game-changer that evening in our duel of willpower.

Sensing Mominda's transient hesitation, I pressed home my advantage, and delivered the *coup de grâce*.

'So, I'm allowed to eat beef.'

Instinct told Mominda that I was being cheeky, that I was stretching veracity when I claimed to link my lineage to Derozio, but he also knew of my schooling at St Xavier's, which had given me the advantage of a broad and inclusive education, and that those of us with such an eclectic upbringing considered ourselves the intellectual and moral progeny of our hero, Henry Derozio.

The creases of concern and doubt that had earlier furrowed Mominda's brow melted away. Under the weight of my clinching 'I'm related to Derozio' argument, he decided to concede with grace.

Mominda suppressed a smile; a look passed between us and an unspoken contract was agreed – one that implied an impish complicity.

'OK then,' he said, as we went back from the kitchen to join the others waiting at the dining table. 'But only Gautam and I are allowed beef this evening.'

*

My next memorable interaction with Mominda occurred a few years later, when I had qualified and was a junior house surgeon in general surgery. It was a sweltering summer night in Calcutta and we were both on-call for surgical emergencies at the Medical College Hospital. A young woman was admitted after midnight, gravely ill from blood poisoning that had started with a neglected kidney infection. The high fever made her eyes unnaturally bright like pinpoints of light in a wan, stretched face. Her fervid skin was waxy with a sweaty sheen. She was hardly conscious and clearly needed urgent surgery.

As the junior-most doctor of the surgical team, I was sent off to rouse the senior surgeon-on-call, our Mominda. I found him where I expected to find him, coolly sprawled on a clean white sheet laid out on the scrubbed floor of the empty operating theatre, the only place with air-conditioning, the only haven of refuge in the broiling stagnant air inside the casualty block of Medical College Hospital, that oppressive May night in Calcutta.

In the tenebrous light and the stillness of the operating theatre, as I gently yet urgently roused my snoring mentor, in those moments of half-sleep and semi-consciousness, between repose and alert, Mominda made two insightful observations.

He sat up tousle-headed, and said with great seriousness, 'Gautam, always remember, urological surgery is the most hazardous form of surgery.'

To this, he added after an imperceptible pause, 'Before starting an operation, quietly utter under your breath - "*Bismillah*" [by the grace of God].'

In his caution regarding urological surgery, Mominda was in august company. As far back as the fourth century BC, Hippocrates had cautioned against operating for bladder stones. In his famous "Oath of Medical Ethics", the great physician of ancient Greece had warned that bladder wounds were lethal. Being someone who relished a challenge, I did indeed go on to specialise in urological surgery. My preparation started that very night as I assisted Mominda in a difficult nephrectomy to remove the young woman's pus-filled kidney, an operation that saved her life.

As for the other admonishment, it was not unnatural or contentious to adopt and follow my mentor's salutation to God using the words of a different faith, as it was my good fortune to have received the benefit of a liberal education.

My own beloved parents as well as the Jesuit Fathers at St Xavier's School had inculcated in us a love and respect for faith, indeed all faiths. Ram, the name of God for Hindus, and Rahim, that for Muslims, were equally dear to us. So that which started off as a harmless more became over the years of pretty much regular usage. Not quite like the WHO checklist of patient safety at the start of an operating list, nonetheless a comforting beginning to the day's work and related challenges.

As a senior consultant surgeon, I still find that a murmured *Bismillah* steadies the mind whilst scrubbing for an operation. Even more comforting is the full invocation of *Bismillah ir Rehman ir Rahim*, the resonance of which is poorly conveyed in the commonly understood translation – "In the name of God, most Gracious, most Compassionate".

Moreover, when faced on the operating table with a particularly portentous situation, such as when that pesky Satinsky arterial clamp has slipped, and certainly before the critical step of securing a ligature across the main renal artery during radical nephrectomy, an extra *Bismillah* is always offered.

*

I will ask you dear reader, to draw your own conclusions. Is religion a salve, an anodyne in the travails of ordinary human existence? I do not know. I am equally unsure whether Marx's comparison of deeply held faith to opium is correct.

What I do know for certain, is that many surgeons the world over say a quiet prayer from time to time. If such "religious" observance were to be considered, according to Marx's apparent definition as substance abuse [sic], and therefore condemned, it would make life awkward.

After all, it is strictly against the service rules of the NHS to partake of any narcotic, of whatsoever provenance, before starting an operation!

CHAPTER 20

In Britain, I am often asked by friends about my early years in Calcutta. More recently, my grandchildren, born in English towns and shires, have started to demand storytelling with an Indian flavour. The tale of Rajmistri seems to be a favourite and has struck many a chord.

Rajmistri (master mason)

Calcutta – 1965

May is the melting month of Calcutta. At the height of the scalp-splitting midday sun, shoes and sandals squelch, trying to free themselves from the suction pull of the molten tar. People dissolve in becks and runnels of salty sweat. Stray dogs, cats, sacred cows – all seek out shadows, shelters and enclaves. Raucous crows fall silent in the dead heat. There is no breeze to provide a modicum of relief, not even a susurrus.

At high noon, everyone seeks refuge indoors, unless some imperative drags them into the roiling furnace outside.

I myself was indoors, revising for the forthcoming Senior Cambridge examinations of high school. My study was on the top floor of our three-storey mansion in the Ballygunge area of South Calcutta. The yearly income of the upper middle-class householders in this suburb was far above the national average of 1960s India.

My father was a London-qualified senior chartered accountant at the British firm of Lovelock and Lewes. My equally well-educated mother was Head of Chemistry at the nearby Kamala Girl's High School. As their only offspring, my parents had not scrimped on my education. Sure, they ensured careful husbandry for luxuries such as holidays and the family motorcar. But their son's education had been the first, the most important and well-endowed item of the household budget.

I had a Jewish governess from the age of three, till I entered primary school two years later – thirty-year-old Esther Cohen was a slim-wristed woman of dove-white complexion, who would slip me the occasional bar of Cadbury's milk chocolate and watch with a smile my childish eagerness to rip the silver foil.

She would ensure that it was English and not the vernacular that expressed my thoughts and coloured my dreams. She held me spellbound with tales and fables from the Old Testament.

It was therefore with ease that I was able to enter the elite fee-paying "boys only" school of St Xavier's, where the medium of instruction was English.

St Xavier's School in Park Street, the *sahib-para* (literally "secluded enclave of English sahibs") of Calcutta, is to this day acknowledged to be the pre-eminent boy's school, the Eton of Calcutta and the entire east of India. An ethos of excellence is inculcated early by the awe-inspiring Jesuit Fathers, who long years ago had set out from the harbours of Antwerp and Zeebrugge, leaving behind homes and families in France, Belgium and Luxembourg.

The missionary order of the Society of Jesus that commanded their spiritual allegiance had sent them to the Far East to educate Indian boys in distant Calcutta. The school motto is N*ihil Ultra*, nothing beyond. Being a Xaverian confers two critical advantages in India. First being the proficiency in English – the language of power and control, university education, and science and commerce. Then there are the tangible and intangible privileges attendant with membership of an elite institution, a kind of masonic opening of solid doors.

*

I was in my last year of high school, in the science stream of St Xavier's prestigious Senior Cambridge curriculum. The final examinations were due in December. A high first division was imperative for a coveted place for admission either in Medical College or to a pure science BSc course at Presidency College. The competition for both was fierce.

Every available hour in the day had to be pressed into revision. My study was equipped with all the accoutrements conducive for scholarship. The room itself with pastel walls was comfortably spacious, such that the bookcases, desk and chairs, the glass-fronted steel almirah were not crowded. Natural light streamed in through the two large windows that opened on one side. Fluorescent strip lights and the hinged table-lamp were switched on only in the evening. The blades of the overhead Crompton ceiling fan billowed a cooling draught.

The open doorway connecting my study to the inner corridor admitted our indulgent home-help lady and my mother bearing regular supplies of refreshment – succulent cubes of ripe juicy mango, piping hot vegetable pakoras, aromatic skewers of chilli chicken, smoky glass bottles of Coca-Cola fresh out of the chiller cabinet. Everything was done to ensure that I could devote maximum uninterrupted time to study.

It was a pampered tabernacle for a cossetted sixteen-year-old.

Despite all the appurtenances and all the attention, my mind was resentful towards the deadlines imposed by our exacting schoolmasters. Sternest of them all was Father Louis Hincq, our headmaster and English Literature tutor. That afternoon, I was required to complete a critique on the literary and social merits of *The Merchant of Venice*.

I found myself unmoved by the troubles of Antonio and Bassanio. I was unimpressed by the manipulative logic employed by the comely Portia, disguised as a male scholar of law in the court of the Doge of Venice. The debate as to whether Shylock was the real victim, and the implied polemic of an undercurrent of anti-Semitism that pervaded the play, gave me the beginnings of a headache.

I forced myself to make a start and write a few lines, which lacked conviction. A muted sound just outside my window disturbed my fragile attention. It was the sound of men's voices. It was not too loud. Under ordinary circumstances this would hardly have been a distraction. After all, Calcutta was never a quiet city.

Tradesmen and hawkers walking up and down the streets perforce have to shout from their lung bases to drown the competition. The incessant blasts of car horns and the loud metallic tings of bicycle and rickshaw bells do not reduce accidents but add to the cacophony. The scraping of metal buckets and pails on the pavement set your teeth on edge; the splashing of water from the roadside tube wells, the insistent cawing of crows, and chirping of the tiny mynahs, all contribute to the clamour. Everybody speaks as though the listener is tone deaf. Calcuttans are accustomed to a base level of noise with periodic accretions. It is all part of life in our chaotic hometown – our beloved Calcutta – maximum city, maximum noise, maximum emotion, maximum everything.

My desire to abandon Shakespeare and my essay made me rise and look out of the window. There were five men speaking at just below eye level. They were not inside the house next door; these men were on it. The mansion, a near mirror-image of ours, belonged to the Mukherjees, our neighbours. Mr Atin Mukherjee, a successful tax advocate practising in the Calcutta High Court was having work carried out to the exterior of his house.

The five men were the team of workers doing the job. They were attached to the side of the Mukherjee mansion like Spiderman. The only difference was that instead of using suction pads on webbed hands and feet, these workmen were defying gravity and at third-floor level, a 40-foot drop, by perching on the lattices of a scaffold, a structure that was not a steel frame of geometric longitudes and latitudes. This was the echt Indian version with bamboo poles instead of steel pipes. The criss-cross of bamboo poles were secured with rough coir roping.

The men perched on this contraption along with their

tools and tins of Dulux acrylic emulsion didn't have safety harnesses around their waists or helmets on their bare heads. Grimy headbands kept out rivulets of sweat from stinging their eyes. Lean and wiry, their sinews stood out like ropes; skin was burnt a polished ochre from working punishing hours under the pitiless Indian sun; they were the embodiment of spartan endurance. The men wore coloured patterned *lungis* – indigenous sarongs, ruched up and tightly wound at the waist and upper thighs with no flapping ends to snag.

The men were of varying ages ranging from teenagers not much older than myself, to early thirties.

Their task that afternoon was to complete painting the section of the wall that was level with my study. At day's end this subaltern brigade would collect a modest daily wage and be provided with a ploughman's meal of roti, daal, a vegetable preparation with green chillies and raw onions, as well as the de rigeur mug of hot milky tea, heaped with sugar.

Their leader was the Rajmistri (master mason). A man becomes a Rajmistri only after years of hard toil acquiring skills in labour-intensive workmanship. He also possesses and provides leadership. His men look up to him as their chieftain.

The Rajmistri leading the work on the Mukherjee house was in his mid-forties, my father's age at the time. This man was the only one wearing a fenestrated singlet above his *lungi* and was clean-shaven. Rajmistri had strong shoulders. He directed his men with gentle commands and sparse admonition. There was also some comradely banter in their workmen's argot.

This was the frisson that had broken my concentration. The exchange had not been discordant or in coarse language. There was nothing that could not have been ignored like all the other external timpani-rolls. It's just that my concentration was longing to be broken, like a child with a pin eyeing an oversized balloon.

Irritated, I went over to the window and addressed Rajmistri.

'Now look, I'm trying to study for my exams, you men are making too much noise.'

My tone was imperious, the voice hectoring. For "you" I had used "*tumi*", the Bengali equivalent of the diminutive "*tu*" in French, rather than the more respectful "*apni*" or "*vous*" towards a man my father's age. I was fully aware that I was being unreasonable, churlish in my adolescent peeve and peremptory in manner.

My words stilled the conversation as abruptly as a drop of sulphuric acid turns a strip of litmus paper bright red. A blinding silence followed, a silence that obliterated all senses and froze thought. A moment distilled pure and immobilised as though in aspic.

Rajmistri looked at me with incredulity. My extraordinary rudeness seemed to have robbed him of speech. His men lowered their gaze and waited. They would not have dreamt of uttering a single word before Rajmistri had spoken. He was their undisputed Caliph. Opening their mouths before he had articulated a rejoinder would have been unacceptably disrespectful and would have undermined their chief's authority. The decision on the nature of response to my discourtesy verging on the insulting was his alone. They waited in stunned silence.

The entire exchange had occupied no more than five, perhaps six, seconds. Yet to my mind the moment of silence lengthened almost to eternity. Rajmistri's tranquil countenance did not alter as he came to a decision. I would not have been taken aback if he had put my insolence in its rightful place with a sharp retort.

Instead, with a calm and measured voice, he said to his charges, 'Quiet you fellows, no more chit chat, Dadababu [literally translated – young master] has to read his exam books.'

*

I write this story towards the zenith of my career as a consultant surgeon and as I start my seventh decade of life. I rail at that spoilt adolescent's puerile behaviour, but much more, marvel at the lonely struggle that must have raged in Rajmistri's breast that sultry afternoon in Calcutta, the difficult choice that he had to confront, all on his own.

To this day, through the scrim of time, I can touch the turmoil in his mind. His team, those who looked up to him for leadership and direction, had awaited his response. Time had stood still whilst he had battled within.

The concept of inner struggle is age-old. It is the central theme of the *Bhagavad Gita*, where the warrior prince Arjuna questions the ethics and justification of war; it is in the Bible, as exquisitely endured by St Paul in Romans 7; and is exemplified as *Jihad e Akbar*, the greater Jihad, that of the spirit, in Islam.

In all the spiritual teachings, the universal message

that comes through enjoins man to subdue his baser self, and rise to a morally elevated ideal.

That afternoon, long years ago in Calcutta, Rajmistri had battled with his inner self. And in his lonely struggle, he had abjured the temptation of the petty, and showed the courage to achieve that which is truly noble.

CHAPTER 21

A tryst with destiny

Trevor's story
Croydon – 2013

It was another Monday morning at our busiest urology outpatient clinic at Croydon University Hospital, with more than 40 patients referred by GPs, other departments and from A&E. Many of our older male patients had been sent for investigation of suspected prostate cancer.

I finished a quick ward round in Bensham 2 and headed down the corridor of the Surgical Block towards Main Outpatients, moving to one side as a squad of junior doctors importantly dangling stethoscopes and green venepuncture tourniquets hurtled by on a busy hospital round. I walked past a row of seated men and women silently waiting their turn outside the phlebotomy room. It was June, the promise of summer. Through the corridor's floor to ceiling window panes, the elms and sycamores in the main courtyard were abundant with buds and the rich emerald leaves of spring.

At ten-past-eight, it was still too early for the clinics to be filling up. The new dark brown Rexine chairs in the reception area were empty.

The outpatient staff were, however, busy at their workstations. Jena, the clerk at the appointments desk, her short curls tinted purple that week, looked up from her computer screen. She smiled as she saw me and said, 'Hi Mr Das. You're in your favourite room 8 today. I'll bring over your clinic list and notes in a sec.'

Jim, our ever-cheerful volunteer, was also in early. Still energetic in his eighties, Jim was forever ready with a courteous welcome. He asked, 'Did you get to the Eurotunnel in time last Friday, Mr Das?'

'Just made it Jim, thanks for asking,' I replied. I had so many times tried to get Jim to have a chair to rest his veteran legs. Like the diligent sentry however, Jim resolutely preferred to be upstanding all the while as he handed out tickets and welcomed visitors to outpatients, so reminiscent of the beaming senior citizens dressed as Mounties in airport arrivals at Toronto and Vancouver.

I nodded to Karen, the new Outpatient Sister with a B.Sc. in nursing, sitting in her office, spreadsheets spilling over her desk, as I walked past to my clinic room.

Soon there was a knock on the door.

Angi had arrived armed with bulging plastic folders, colour-coded, containing accumulated paperwork – part of the Monday morning ritual.

The green folder was the thickest, so full that it couldn't be snapped shut. It was crammed with referral letters. The orange folder – not far behind in substance – contained correspondence and pathology reports. The white folder had last week's clinic and operation letters to be checked and signed.

The lilac folder was my favourite. It housed invitations to attend scientific meetings and deliver lectures, personal letters of appreciation, occasionally a bonhomie spoiling missive like the one last month from the parking office admonishing me for using the space opposite the boiler, the day I was late for theatres.

'Don't forget David Prescott, Senior Registrar from Barts is coming to see you about the consultant job this afternoon,' Angi said from the door on her way back to the urology office. How imperceptibly the wheels of life advance – nearly twenty-five years in one place, a settled existence despite the leaps and the stumbles, the thrill of building a new department, the sorrow of a lost ward, of seeing beds whittled away, the joy of trainees who have stretched the line beyond your own, remorse for the ones you couldn't help. You think you have found in that one place, a provisional stillness, a sanctuary against time itself. And then the moment comes to move on, to move out, to make way. Yes, it's true – *change is the only constant thing in life.*

I heard subtle sounds outside the door. Soft ushering voices, a chair leg scraping.

It was nearly nine, time to call in the first patient.

I opened the clinic door.

Seated outside my clinic room was an upright elderly gentleman smartly dressed in steel blue jacket and regimental tie, and next to him, touching shoulders, a much younger woman with chestnut hair. They both looked up as I called the name.

This was Trevor Broadbent's second appointment in the urology clinic and his first consultation with me. On his previous visit he'd been seen by one of my colleagues.

Mr Broadbent had now come back, a week later, for a decision to be made.

I held open the door to invite them in. Trevor Broadbent's handshake was firm as I introduced myself. The young lady at his side explained, 'I'm Penny, Trevor's step-daughter. I've come down from Shropshire to be with him today.'

A quick glance at his notes reminded me that Trevor was well into his eighties. His GP had run routine blood tests as part of his regular check-up. Although Trevor hadn't complained of any waterworks problem, the GP had ticked the box for PSA (prostate specific antigen), the prostate blood test.

The PSA had come back at 7.8, just that bit higher than the 5.0 which would have been fine for his age. The above normal reading signified the possibility of prostate cancer. The GP had promptly despatched an urgent suspected cancer (USC) referral.

At the first clinic appointment, Trevor had undergone a rectal examination. His prostate was slightly enlarged, not unusual in men over sixty. There were no suspicious nodules, and overall the prostate felt smooth and supple, not firm or hard, which would have suggested cancer.

The urologist had told him, 'Your prostate doesn't feel worrying, and you don't have any symptoms Mr Broadbent, but your PSA is a bit high.' He had gone on to warn, 'We have to consider a biopsy.' Trevor was then told what the biopsy would entail.

'I need to think about this, and talk it over with my family,' Trevor had said.

He was provided with an information leaflet and a number to call Maureen, our clinical nurse specialist, if later he had more questions.

Trevor Broadbent had come on his own for that first clinic appointment. His wife had died a few years earlier, and he lived alone. The chill words "prostate cancer", the prospect of "needle biopsy", all those fearful "possible" complications graphically listed in the information leaflet unsettled him. He picked up the telephone that evening, glanced at the eleven digits on a slip of paper he'd been given earlier with the information leaflet, and dialled instead a number in Shropshire.

*

Prostate biopsies are done under local anaesthetic in the X-Ray department. The procedure usually takes about twenty minutes, and is performed using an ultrasound probe with attached needle biopsy device inserted inside the rectum. As the prostate gland sits right in front of the rectum, it can be felt, scanned and biopsied through the adjacent rectal wall. We take tiny thread-like snippets of prostate tissue and send them to the path lab.

'You'll notice some blood in the urine and semen Mr Broadbent,' he'd been advised.

What was more ominous was the statement, 'We'll give you antibiotics, but there's still a small chance you may get a bad infection. If you feel unwell or shivery when you're home, you must come straight back to casualty.'

This "bad infection" can mutate into overwhelming sepsis in a minute percentage, usually the very elderly and those whose immune systems are compromised – a calamity that can lead to death from multi-organ failure.

I also noted from his drug history that Trevor was

taking warfarin for a mild stroke that he'd suffered and recovered from, a few years ago. Warfarin, a powerful blood-thinner, significantly increases the risk of excessive bleeding during any surgical procedure. Accordingly, we'd have to stop Trevor's warfarin a few days before the biopsy, which in turn would have its own risks, making things that bit more complicated.

Before doing a biopsy, an MRI scan would have helped as MRI (magnetic resonance imaging) provides excellent high definition pictures of the prostate architecture. Areas suspicious of cancer appear as black holes. We can also see breaches in the capsule that surrounds the prostate, enlarged lymph nodes and bone marrow changes, all of which indicate advanced prostate cancer.

An MRI that didn't show any overt worrying changes, though not absolutely excluding cancer, would've been re-assuring. We would have felt less pressurised to do a biopsy.

It was frustrating, but we couldn't do an MRI for Trevor as he had a cardiac pacemaker. This is an absolute contra-indication to magnetic resonance, as powerful magnets and metallic objects fastened to the heart do not make a prudent combination!

*

Trevor came straight to the point. 'We can't make up our minds about the biopsy, Mr Das.'

'Dad's eighty-seven. He lives on his own…' Penny looked at her step-father. 'What we'd really like is for you to tell us what *you* think we should do.'

230

The quandary I had with Trevor was this – in order to confirm or exclude the diagnosis of prostate cancer, I'd have to subject this elderly man with a pacemaker and on warfarin to an invasive procedure with the risk of a lethal complication.

Prostate cancer is much more prevalent in older men, many of whom do not require active treatment. This is because many prostate cancers are extremely slow-growing. They can co-exist with good health for many years without causing any detriment. We can do more harm by ill-thought out heavy-handed treatment, given that no treatment is entirely free of side-effects and complications. Most of these somnolent prostate cancers can simply be kept under surveillance with regular blood tests just as we do for diet-controlled type 2 diabetes and some cases of mild hypertension. When necessary, we could always intervene if the check-up blood tests were to suggest (by way of a rising PSA level) that the cancer was becoming hostile.

Would this watchful approach not be appropriate for Trevor? Did I really need to biopsy this man?

In order to relax the tension, I switched the conversation to matters unrelated to medical issues. Over the years, I have learned that it always helps to listen about people's lives, their work and hobbies, not just their medical complaints. It softens any perceived "I'm a busy consultant" image. Moreover, when faced with a tough clinical choice, it has often afforded me those valuable extra minutes of thinking time. And of course, life isn't just the practice of medicine and surgery. Many reading suggestions, of history books and novels, have come from conversations with my patients in clinics and wards. I have had books ranging from religion to philosophy lent to me, some even with prolific pencil ticks and underlines. An alert octogenarian, a retired schoolteacher who had taught literature, would unfailingly come for his outpatient appointments, bringing in his folio case, carefully tucked away newspaper and magazine cuttings ranging from online courses and book reviews to notifications of BBC History weekends.

From his date of birth, I saw that Trevor would have been twenty when the Second World War ended. He may have been a participant in the final apocalyptic years. Many of my elderly patients, both men and women, have a rich trove of wartime experiences both on the battlefield as well the home front. Encouraging them to share their wartime experiences unlocks a memory bank, of a time when they were young and zestful, when they'd lived through seismic times, and had extolled their contempt for death.

Only a few weeks earlier, a war veteran had related his story as a paratrooper on Special Ops. He brought to life the drama and adrenaline rush of a night-time drop on a desolate field behind enemy lines in occupied northern France. He remembered with vivid detail the inky black midnight when his parachute billowed down.

'The moon was on furlough that night Mr Das, thank God.'

He could even recall the slightly pungent earthy smell of the freshly furrowed soil that had cushioned his fall. Recounting those heady times had animated the seemingly phlegmatic nonagenarian into the vigorous young wartime soldier that lived within.

Trevor too had a story to tell.

'I joined the RAF when I was called up. We were sent all the way to Manitoba for training. England was too dangerous. Goering's men were still coming over.'

'You must've learnt to fly Hurricanes and Spitfires?' I asked.

'No. I ended up in a Lancaster, as "Tail-end Charlie".'

He narrated the experience of sitting in the rear gun turret of a four-engined heavy bomber as it thundered off on a fiery mission. He recounted the knot of fear deep in his belly as the enemy coastline approached; the starbursts of flak, the unrelenting tension of fearful expectation – that of his vision suddenly eaten up by the spectral shape of a minatory Luftwaffe night fighter, hoping that his own taut reflexes would be sharper than those of his adversary.

His face relaxed when he said, 'The *relief* I felt every time my plane abruptly lurched up. That was our signal – the payload was down, it was time to turn round and go home, mug of tea and a nip of rum.'

'That must've been your sharpest memory?'

'Oh no. The thing I remember most was the freezing cold in my Perspex bubble. It was sub-zero, like a mortuary.'

I congratulated him on his survival.

'Yes, I made it. I'm still here. Many of my mates didn't. You see the average life expectancy of a Lancaster rear gunner in the Second War was only six weeks.' In his wallet was his talisman, his precious St Christopher, which he took out and carefully laid on the table. Yet I saw in his eyes the secret grief of lost comrades, the mourning of growing old alone.

There was a knock on the connecting door, a barely

perceptible pause, and our Specialist Registrar Jonathan entered. He unobtrusively collected four sets of waiting notes and took them to his clinic room next door, thoughtfully taking off the pressure on me to hurry the consultation.

Penny picked up the thread of conversation. 'Well, you've certainly made him open up Mr Das. My dad hasn't spoken about his war antics for a long time now.'

Trevor added, 'You wouldn't have been born then Mr Das, but your parents and family must have gone through some tough times during the war. India was critical for our Allied strategy against the Japanese.'

'You know,' I said, 'my father told me many a story of the war. The one about the RAF I seem to remember best was of a young fighter pilot called… Pring? Yes, that's it – Maurice Pring. Though he was just out of his teens, Maurice Pring was an ace of the Burma campaign. He saved Calcutta from Japanese bombs. My father described him as Calcutta's own toreador of the night skies.'

My memory felt the evoked tug of a school trip with our Rector, Father Joris, to the Commonwealth War cemetery in South Calcutta's Bhowanipore – of a weathered alabaster headstone, an Englishman's name, just twenty-two years separating the dates, a dew-fresh wreath of roses, crimson as heart's blood.

'Oh yes, and I also remember my father saying with pride that for downing three Imperial Japanese bombers in one night, before the noon of his own tryst with eternity, Flight Sergeant Pring was awarded the Distinguished Flying Medal.'

Penny glanced at her step-father and smiled, an

affectionate smile, in which I sensed the unspoken, possibly a shared knowledge.

I gently steered the conversation back to Trevor's PSA. By then I had gained enough thinking time. I had come to a decision. High on my mind was the thought that it would be such a shame if this Trojan who had survived such odds were to be felled by cowardly sepsis or bleeding.

'I think I know a way of looking after you without a biopsy. Let me run this past our prostate team, but I'm pretty sure they'll agree with me.'

I arranged to see Trevor and Penny again in two weeks.

I brought the case to our MDM.

Although I was the designated Lead for Urology Cancer, I was simply *primus inter pares*, first among equals. Everyone's opinion carried equal weight and it was my role to ensure a consensus. In Trevor's case, the oncologists and my surgical colleagues agreed that my proposed plan of action made perfect sense.

I had suggested that, as with similar cases, we simply monitor Trevor by regularly checking his PSA. If the levels remained steady, we wouldn't need to intervene. If there was a worrying rise in his PSA, we could treat him with tablets and injections to control the prostate cancer.

Two weeks later, I met up again with Trevor and Penny. This time, Maureen was by my side in clinic.

'I've got good news. You're not having a biopsy,' I started.

Maureen took over, 'Mr Das discussed you with all his colleagues at our multi-disciplinary meeting last week. Everyone agreed that we should keep an eye on you with regular blood tests.'

Penny turned to her step-father and squeezed his hand.

I picked up the Dictaphone, 'What I'm going to do, is write to your GP and ask him to check your PSA again in three months. If it's much the same as your last one, we'll continue with six monthly tests. At any stage your GP can refer you back to us if your PSA starts to go up.'

The couple in front listened attentively, but now with the tranquil expression of happy tidings.

'By the way sir, do you like tomatoes?' Maureen asked.

'I do actually, is that important?'

'Yes, they're good for you. Tomatoes contain lycopenes, which are very good for the prostate. As are pumpkin seeds and broccoli.'

'He's likes his greens and veg. And now I'll make sure he sprinkles pumpkin seeds on his porridge,' Penny promised with a smile.

*

Two weeks later, when Angi brought in the folders, I found a thick A5 size cream envelope in the lilac personal folder. The writing on the envelope with my name and hospital address was steady and strong.

As I tore open the envelope a letter fell out. It was hand-written in fountain pen ink. It was a letter from Trevor. He thanked me for the clear explanation, for helping him come to a decision that he felt comfortable and confident with. He also conveyed Penny's good wishes to Maureen and myself.

I felt something else inside the envelope, and fished

out a photocopy of an old newspaper cutting. The dateline was April 1945. The grainy sepia image showed the face and torso of a young man in uniform with RAF wings; on his chest, a ribbon and a row of medals.

The caption read: "Warrant Officer Hugh Trevor Broadbent awarded Distinguished Flying Cross for exceptional bravery in the face of enemy action".

The note and photocopy are carefully saved in my collection of personal letters.

Acknowledgements

The Matador team have been brilliant in every which way. Lauren, Katherine, Alice, Rosie, Stephanie and Jasmin, thank you for your professionalism, guidance and above all, patience. Imogen, my editor, thank you for pointing out the unclear and incomplete, and for teaching me the correct use of ellipsis and square brackets amongst my several other shortcomings.

Dr Pat Walton, my consultant anaesthetist of over twenty years, has been much more than a colleague. So too has been the quietly effective Dr Murali. An anaesthetist is a surgeon's guide, friend and conscience-keeper. It is wise to choose well, and once chosen, to respect, nurture and enhance that relationship.

My first wife Baidehi, who pulled me through my doubts and despairs of medical school years, helped me qualify and then complete my MS thesis. She softened the upheaval of leaving home in India, and absorbed the shock of adjustment in a new country. During all those years of training, she moved household from the Midlands to the West Country, from Wales to Yorkshire and finally Croydon, single-handedly bringing up our two children and all our pets. She remains a concerned well-wisher.

My son Indy, a successful family care physician in western Canada, I would like to thank for his unwavering attention across the pond on my surgical career and for never letting me dwell on the finishing post.

Asok Banerjee FRCS, Professor of Surgery, Medical College Hospitals, Calcutta, my role model, my hero.

John Wickham FRCS, Director of the Institute of Urology, London, my mentor who encouraged my research and gave me that critical career break. He showed me how to bend light and look beyond obstacles. My English father.

All my wonderful friends at Croydon University Hospital – Angela, Charity, Hilda, Margaret, Novvi in theatres, Valerie and Chris in the admissions office, Paulene, Rozina, Bina, Elvie amongst many in outpatients. Our indispensable clinical nurse specialists, Vitra and Maureen. My secretaries Julie, Pat and Angi, angels of patience and shock absorbers of deadlines. The medical, surgical, anaesthetic and radiology colleagues too numerous to mention individually. Paulette and Leilani in Shirley Oaks Hospital theatres. Denise, Anita, Julie, Tracey, Lesley, Julia, Val in Shirley Oaks outpatients for making sure that all the investigation results were available from path labs and nuclear medicine departments, from MDMs and X-Ray. Brother surgeons of the pelvic cancer team at St George's, the anaesthetists and theatre and ward nurses who made a visiting surgeon from Croydon welcome for those five great years.

Mark McCrum and Steve Attridge, tutors at the Guardian writing masterclasses. Tom Bromley, tutor at the Faber academy. All my fellow students who killed my clichés and adjectives while encouraging me to get the phrases and sentences out on paper.

Susan, my second wife, has never let me compromise with anything less than perfect, and so it was with my writing and re-writing. She made sure that every word and every sentence was as good as it could be. Her breath rests in every page. By the time the drafts had piled to double digits, I could happily have flung the computer a great distance. Her quiet strength prevented surrender to, "I can't do this," and a book emerged from its chrysalis, that approached anything close to doing justice to the people about whom it has been written.